ENERCELL®
BATTERY
GUIDEBOOK

By
Master Publishing, Inc

SECOND EDITION

A DIVISION OF TANDY CORPORATION
FORT WORTH, TEXAS 76102

THIS BOOK WAS DEVELOPED AND PUBLISHED BY:
Master Publishing, Inc.
14 Canyon Creek Village, MS 31
Richardson, Texas 75280

DESIGN AND ARTWORK BY:
Plunk Design
Dallas, Texas

PRINTING BY:
Evans Press
Fort Worth, Texas

REGARDING THIS BOOK MATERIAL
This book is for the education of its readers. While reasonable care has been exercised with respect to its accuracy, the publisher and Radio Shack assume no responsibility for errors, omissions or suitability of its contents for any application. Nor do we assume any liability for any damages resulting from use of information in this book. It is the reader's responsibility to determine if the use, sale or manufacture of any device that incorporates information in this book infringes any patents, copyrights or other rights.

Due to the many customer inquiries received by Radio Shack, it is impossible to answer all requests for additional information. This battery book was assembled to provide Radio Shack customers with detailed battery information and data. We will be happy to receive any comments, impressions, suggestions or information concerning this book.

TRADEMARKS
Enercell, Archer, Micronta and Replace-A-Cell are registered trademarks and Hi-capacity is a trademark of the Radio Shack Division of Tandy Corporation.

9 8 7 6 5 4 3 2 1

TABLE OF CONTENTS

Radio Shack Battery Club

Get a free general purpose Enercell each month. Pick up your battery club card at any Radio Shack store. Present the card to the salesperson and receive one free battery each month from the following sizes: General Purpose D, C, AA or 9 volt battery.

Sample Battery Club Card

Front   Back

Charging of Batteries

- A primary battery is designed to deliver the rated capacity once, then be discarded. It is not capable of being fully recharged.

- Enercell General Purpose (carbon zinc) and Extra Life (zinc chloride) batteries may be revitalized by using a home battery charger.

- Do not try to recharge Enercell Alkaline batteries because these cells may explode and cause personal or physical damage.

- Charge Nickel-Cadmium batteries only in Nickel-Cadmium chargers.

- More information on chargers and charging is found in Chapters 4 and 6.

INTRODUCTION

WHY IT'S IMPORTANT TO KNOW ABOUT BATTERIES

What could be more familiar and commonplace than batteries? Like most dependable things we take them for granted. But when we think about it for a moment, most of us don't know that much about them, and we need to. Think about it: the average U.S. household has over ten battery operated products. Retail stores sell two billion dollars worth of batteries every year. Batteries go into everything from flashlights, radios, tape recorders, calculators, watches, clocks, to portable TVs, cordless telephones, power tools, alarm systems, smoke detectors, and home computer equipment. Battery backup is depended on to save the memory contents in appliances like programmable telephones and digital stereo tuners whenever power fails.

This guidebook can help you become more knowledgeable about batteries; especially Radio Shack's Enercell batteries. Whether you are an electronics professional, into a technical hobby, curious, or just want to become a better battery buyer, this book will help you. Having over a hundred pages of specifications and data, virtually makes it a designer's reference book.

The guidebook covers eight basic types of electrochemical batteries; Carbon Zinc, Zinc Chloride, Alkaline, Nickel-Cadmium, Mercury, Silver, Lithium and Zinc Air. You'll learn how a battery works. You will get descriptions, constructions, and performance data for all Enercell batteries. A heavy battery user can learn the advantages of owning and operating a battery tester. Learn the difference between revitalizing and recharging a battery.

Understanding the pros and cons of the different batteries will let you match the best one to the job. Just studying the battery selection table alone can help you become a very wise consumer.

The bottom line is that by investing a little time in reading this guidebook, you can learn to choose batteries that will last longer, improve performance, and save you money.

Chapter 1

BASIC DRY CELL BATTERY

Allesanaro Volta is the man that gave us the word volt, our unit for electrical pressure or electromotive force. In 1789 he took a copper rod and a zinc rod and immersed them both in an acetic acid solution. He had just constructed the first battery cell with the first electrolyte. The copper and zinc rods were the electrodes, positive and negative. The acid started to eat away the zinc rod, while the copper rod captured the energy released from the action. A voltage developed between the two electrodes. Volta had invented the battery. The electrochemical principles that he discovered are still the foundation for the battery industry.

Seventy-nine years went by before George Leclanch developed a practical cell. He used manganese-dioxide powder as the positive electrode instead of copper; he kept the zinc. He used sal ammoniac (ammonium chloride) in water for his electrolyte. A porous cup held the powder which surrounded a carbon collector. Leclanch put the whole business, or the cell, into a glass jar and invented the first wet battery.

The first dry cell battery was manufactured in 1888 under the auspices of a Dr. Gassner. It was to become the prototype for the dry cell battery industry. Gassner used zinc to hold all of the components and kept zinc for the negative electrode as well. The electrolyte material was absorbed by a porous medium. He also added zinc chloride to the electrolyte which cut back zinc corrosion when the cell was inactive. This was a big step for longer battery storage life. Now, for the first time a dry cell battery was a neat, tightly sealed package, almost ready for mass production. It didn't take long. Batteries were first mass produced in 1890 by the National Carbon Company at their plant in Cleveland, Ohio. Later they became the industrial giant known as Union Carbide.

Since 1890, leak resistant dry cell batteries have enjoyed an ever growing pervasiveness with only modest changes in design, until about fifteen years ago. That's when our high technology thrust really began to kick into high gear. Since then new batteries have been invented and fresh designs and improvements have been arriving regularly. Witness the huge variety of button cell batteries used to supply power to the miniature circuits found in so many electronic products. Batteries continue to undergo a renaissance. Users, both technical and consumer, will be well served to stay abreast.

Pick up a General Purpose Enercell battery. Beneath the label is a cylinder, a can made of zinc. Inside the can is an electrolyte separator and it's saturated with an electrolyte paste. In the center of the can is a carbon rod. The space all around is filled with manganese-dioxide cathode mix. These are the basic players, the ingredients that will supply the power inside the battery. See *Figure 1-1*.

Now here's what happens. An electrochemical reaction takes place inside the zinc can to produce electrical energy. A chemical reaction takes place between the electrolyte paste and the manganese-dioxide causing the zinc can to dissolve. This three-way chemical reaction produces negative ions which electrically gather at the zinc chloride. Meanwhile, the carbon rod is a terminal. It is positive, gathering the positive ions produced in the chemical reaction. The generation and gathering of the positive and negative elements creates the battery energy.

As energy is used, the effectiveness of the basic battery ingredients diminish. The zinc gets thinner. Reaction between the zinc and the electrolyte produce byproducts. As these byproducts buildup, the battery's voltage diminishes and performance is curtailed. Also, as manganese-dioxide, the positive material, is used up it too becomes less active. Naturally, the more zinc, manganese-dioxide, and electrolytic chemicals that are in a battery the longer it will last.

The result of the electrochemical reactions is a gradual decline in voltage. *Figure 1-2* shows the typical shape and slope of the battery voltage as discharge takes place, depending, of course, on the kind of battery, its size, rate of current discharge, operating temperature, and other conditions. Further, all dry cell batteries are not really dry. In fact, some batteries have liquid as an electrolyte. They are completely self contained, leak resistant, and may be used in any position. Internal gases are sealed in and controlled by the chemical mix.

Some batteries use an electrolyte mixed with other ingredients which makes it a paste. Such a paste or gel is absorbed into the separator material and immobilized. Leak resistant batteries such as these are called dry cells.

Figure 1-1. Cell Cross Section

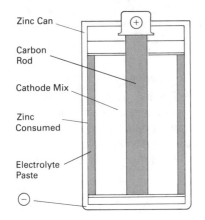

Zinc Can
Carbon Rod
Cathode Mix
Zinc Consumed
Electrolyte Paste

Figure 1-2. Sloping Voltage Discharge Curve

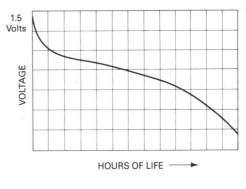

1.5 Volts

VOLTAGE

HOURS OF LIFE ⟶

Chapter 2

FACTORS THAT INFLUENCE BATTERY PERFORMANCE

TERMINAL VOLTAGE UNDER LOAD

Most battery driven products will operate until the battery voltage diminishes to a certain voltage and they cease to operate. This voltage point is called cutoff. Cutoff for a 1.5 volt battery may range from 1.1 volt down to 0.65 volt depending on its use.

When you're designing a product that will be using a battery, set the cutoff voltage as low as possible. This way you will maximize the use of the battery's energy. Whenever the load can handle it, choose the battery with the higher voltage. Selecting the higher voltage battery will provide more efficient use of the battery's available energy.

Battery service life will vary depending on operating schedule, current drain, operating temperature, and cutoff voltage. Capacity is a battery's power potential and is usually better for intermittent duty cycles. Capacity is determined by the relative length of discharge and corresponding recuperation time. Intermittent duty allows access to more of the battery capacity. Continuous duty isn't inefficient, provided the load is light.

Figure 2-1 shows typical service life curves for a general purpose Carbon Zinc battery at different starting current levels. The usable capacity of a general purpose battery is higher with lower current densities, so use as large a battery as possible to minimize current density limitations. Usually you can triple the service life of a battery if you decrease the current drain by half.

TEMPERATURE

General purpose batteries are designed to be used at 70 degrees F (21.1°C). When battery temperature is increased while discharging, its energy output increases. High temperature also reduces storage life, and when the temperature exceeds 125°F (51.7°C) the battery will rapidly deteriorate.

Service life decreases at low temperatures because chemical activity in the battery's cell decreases. This low temperature effect is more predominant at high current drains.

Figure 2-1. Carbon Zinc Size D Discharged 2 Hours/Day @ 70°F (21.1°C)

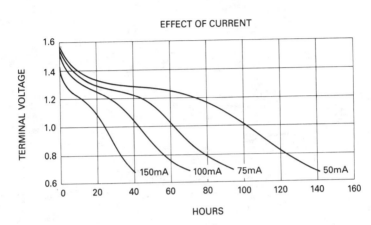

EFFECT OF CURRENT

Terminal voltage also decreases as temperature decreases. Remember, battery terminal voltage under load is more significant than open circuit voltage. *Figure 2-2* shows the effect of temperature on a Carbon Zinc D-cell battery under load. Zinc Chloride batteries generally perform better at low temperature than do Carbon Zinc as shown in *Table A*.

Table A. Temperature Versus Capacity
("D" cells discharged continuously. Load 2.25 ohms — cutoff voltage 0.9V.)

Temperature		Capacity-Value @ 70°F as 100%	
°F	°C	Carbon Zinc	Zinc Chloride
100	37.8	140%	115%
80	26.7	110	105
70	21.1	100	100
60	15.6	90	95
40	4.4	70	85
20	− 6.7	45	70
0	− 17.8	25	45

Storing batteries between 40°F and 50°F can increase the shelf life; but repeated low to high temperature cycling will shorten shelf life.

INTERNAL RESISTANCE

A battery's internal resistance is important when it's going to support high current for a short time. Photo flash and flame ignition are two examples. If internal resistance is too high, terminal voltage will drop rapidly below cutoff at the required current and you probably need a larger battery. A larger battery will reduce internal current density. Internal resistance of fresh Carbon Zinc batteries is quite low and it increases with storage time, use, and low temperatures.

Figure 2-2. Carbon Zinc Size D Continuous Discharge Starting at 667mA

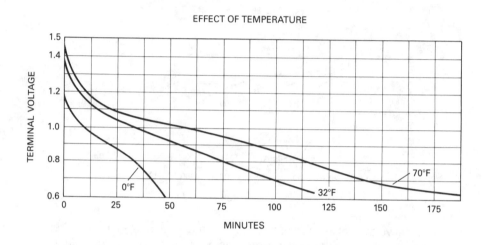

Internal resistance may be measured with a 0.01 ohm load resistor and a dampened ammeter. The 0.01 ohm load represents a short circuit load. Short circuit current is measured and internal resistance is calculated by dividing the open cell voltage by the short circuit current. Short circuit current is not related to service capacity but corresponds to battery size, internal design, and chemical mix. *Table B* gives the short circuit current and internal resistance of several common sizes of Enercell batteries.

Table B. Short Circuit with 0.01 Ohm Load Resistor

| Cell Size | Short Circuit Current (A)/Internal Resistance (Ohms)* | |
	Carbon Zinc	Zinc Chloride
AA	5.3A/0.28 ohms	4.5A/0.33 ohms
C	3.9A/0.39 ohms	6.5A/0.23 ohms
D	5.6A/0.27 ohms	8.5A/0.18 ohms

$$*\text{Internal resistance} = \frac{\text{open circuit voltage}}{\text{short circuit current}}$$

Chapter 3

SELECTING THE RIGHT BATTERY

Choosing the right Enercell battery from among a vast array isn't really that difficult. But it's a whole lot easier when you analyze the job you want the battery to do. If you fill out a checklist like the one below, it will help lead you to the correct battery. And here is another tip — the characteristics of your application may not precisely match the battery design. When this happens, identify your primary need first and select the battery you need on that basis. If you must compromise, do it based on your secondary requirements.

APPLICATION CHECKLIST

1. VOLTAGE
   - ☐ Nominal operating voltage: _____
   - ☐ Minimum operating voltage: _____

2. CURRENT
   - ☐ Initial operating current: _____
   - ☐ Steady operating current: _____

3. OPERATING SCHEDULE
   - ☐ Is it continuous? _____
   - ☐ If not, what is duty cycle?
     Time on: _____
     Time off: _____

4. SERVICE LIFE
   - ☐ What is total life requirement? _____
   - ☐ Ampere-Hour Capacity? — The current requirements (item 2), along with the operating time (item 3) and the service life (item 4) will determine the required capacity.

     Ah = Current (2) _____ × total operating time (3) _____

5. TEMPERATURE

☐ Service temperature will affect service life.
Service temperature: _____
☐ Storage temperature before or during intermittent usage may also affect service life.
Storage temperature: _____

6. PHYSICAL CHARACTERISTICS

☐ Allowable size: _____
☐ Allowable weight will sometimes determine the battery selection at the sacrifice of other optimum characteristics.
Allowable weight: _____
Small batteries with high output capacity usually cost a premium. Larger and heavy batteries sometimes are more reliable if the size and weight can be tolerated.

☐ Preferred battery terminals: _____

7. ENVIRONMENT

☐ Shock: _____
☐ Vibration: _____
☐ Acceleration: _____
☐ Altitude: _____

Unused battery time at any adverse environment conditions including temperature is important.

8. Primary type battery versus secondary (rechargeable) type. The selection of a secondary (rechargeable) battery may make possible a practical selection that could not be achieved if only a primary type battery is considered.
☐ Primary battery selection: _____
☐ Secondary battery selection: _____

Now you are ready to identify your application from *Table C*. Characteristics for eight types of Enercell batteries are found in *Table D*. After you select the type, the specific battery may be found in the technical data section.

METAL-JACKETED BATTERIES

Some Enercell batteries have metal jackets. Data sheets will denote the battery jacket. Battery holders or assemblies using metal jacket batteries should have proper electrical insulation to prevent short circuit of the battery and also provide electrical isolation from other surrounding components. Numerous battery holders for all common size batteries are available from Radio Shack which properly hold and isolate the batteries.

Table C. Dry Cell Batteries

ENERCELL Type	Common Name	Classification	Volts Per Cell*	Characteristics	Applications
General Purpose	Carbon Zinc	Primary	1.5	Low cost, various sizes, discharge voltage falls with usage.	Toys, radios, flashlights, amplifiers, lighting.
Extra Life	Zinc Chloride	Primary	1.5	Service capacity at moderate to high current is 50% greater than Carbon Zinc. Good low temperature performance.	Motor driven toys, cassette players/recorders, radios, clocks, calculators.
Alkaline	Alkaline Manganese Dioxide	Primary	1.5	Good low-temperature characteristics. Discharge voltage falls with usage. Good service under continuous or heavy duty high current usage. May last 5-7 times longer than Carbon Zinc under same loads. More expensive than Carbon Zinc. Has low impedance.	High current drain radios, shavers, electronic photoflash, movie and VCR cameras, toys, tape players/recorders. Walkie-talkies, calculators, motor driven toys, clocks, heavy usage flashlights, radio controlled models.
Rechargeable	Nickel-Cadmium	Secondary	1.2	Maintenance free, hermetically sealed, flat discharge voltage curve with usage. Good high and low temperature performance. Resistant to shock and vibration. Can recharge over and over. High effective capacitance.	Portable power tools, appliances, shavers, toothbrushes, tape recorders, radios, television sets and calculators. Photoflash units, gasoline engine starting, portable communication equipment, radio controlled toys.
Button	Mercuric Oxide	Primary	1.35 and 1.40	Flat discharge voltage characteristics. Excellent high-temperature performance. Same capacity whether used continuously or intermittently.	Hearing aids, watches, calculators, photo electric exposure meters, instruments, pagers, reference voltage source.
Button	Silver Oxide	Primary	1.5	Flat discharge characteristics. Fair low-temperature performance. Similar to Mercuric Oxide except provides higher voltage and higher service capacity to volume ratio.	Hearing aids, watches, calculators, photo electric exposure meters, instruments, pagers, reference voltage source.
Button	Lithium Manganese	Primary	3.0	Good shelf life. Contains high energy density. Wide application temperature range ($-10°F$ to $140°F$). Suitable for heavy drain/pulse discharge uses.	Watches, calculators, cameras, measuring instruments, electronic watches with backlights and alarms.
Button	Zinc Air	Primary	1.45	Excellent shelf life. Lightweight. High energy density. Application temperature range ($32°F$ to $104°F$) Cell must have access to atmospheric oxygen to activate the cell.	Hearing aids, pagers.

*Higher voltage batteries are obtained by internal series connection of cells.

Table D. Typical Battery Characteristics

ENERCELL Type Common Name	General Purpose Carbon Zinc	Extra Life Zinc Chloride	Alkaline Alkaline Manganese Dioxide
Electrochemical System	Zinc-Manganese Dioxide (Called Leclanche or Carbon Zinc)	Zinc-Manganese Dioxide	Zinc-Alkaline Manganese Dioxide
Volts Per Cell	1.5	1.5	1.5
Negative Electrode	Zinc	Zinc	Zinc
Positive Electrode	Manganese Dioxide	Manganese Dioxide	Manganese Dioxide
Electrolyte	Aqueous solution of ammonium chloride and zinc chloride	Aqueous solution of zinc chloride	Aqueous solution of potassium hydroxide
Type	Primary	Primary	Primary
Rechargeability	Poor	Poor	Not Recommended
Recharge Cycles	5-10	5-10	—
Reaction Equation	$2MnO_2 + 2NH_4Cl + Zn \rightarrow ZnCl_2 \cdot 2NH_3 + H_2O + Mn_2O_3$	$8MnO_2 + 4Zn + ZnCl_2 + 9H_2O \rightarrow 8MnOOH + ZnCl_2 \cdot 4ZnO \cdot 5H_2O$	$2Zn + 3MnO_2 \xrightarrow{KOH} 2ZnO + Mn_3O_4$
Typical Service Capabilities	60mAh to 5Ah	150mAh to 7.4Ah	250mAh to 23Ah

Energy Density
  Watt Hour/lb
  Watt Hour/in³
	20
	2
		40
		3
			30-45
			2-3

Practical Current Drain Rates
  Low — Less than 50mA
  High — More than 50mA
	Yes
	100mA/in² Zinc Area
	(D Cell)
		Yes
		150mA/in² Zinc Area
		(D Cell)
			Yes
			200mA/in² Zinc Area
			(D Cell)

Shape of Voltage Discharge Curve	Sloping	Sloping	Sloping

Temperature Range
  Storage
 	
  Operating
	$-40°F(-40°C)$ to 120°F(48.9°C)
	$+20°F(-6.7°C)$ to 130°F(54.4°C)
		$-40°F(-40°C)$ to 160°F(71.1°C)
		$0°F(-17.8°C)$ to 160°F(71.1°C)
			$-40°F(-40°C)$ to 120°F(48.9°C)
			$-20°F(-28.9°C)$ to 130°F(54.4°C)

Temperature Effect on Service Capacity	Poor at low temperature	Better at low termperature than Carbon Zinc.	Good at low temperature
Impedance	Low	Low	Very low
Gassing	Medium	Higher than Carbon Zinc.	Low
Resistance to Shock	Fair to Good	Good	Fair to Good
Operating Cost	Low	Low to Medium	Medium to High
Features	Low cost, numerous sizes.	Service capacity greater than Carbon Zinc. Better low-temperature performance than Carbon Zinc.	High efficiency under moderate to heavy loads. Good low temperature performance. Very low impedance.
Limitations	Efficiency decreases with higher current drains. Poor low-temperature performance.	High temperature performance not much better than Carbon Zinc.	Expensive for low current drain applications.

Rechargeable Nickel-Cadmium	Button Mercuric Oxide	Button Silver Oxide	Button Lithium Manganese	Button Zinc Air
Nickel-Cadmium	Zinc-Mercuric Oxide	Zinc-Silver Oxide	Lithium Manganese Dioxide	Zinc/Oxygen
1.2	1.35 and 1.40	1.5	3.0	1.45
Cadmium	Zinc	Zinc	Lithium	Zinc
Nickelic Hydroxide	Mercuric Oxide	Monovalent Silver Oxide	Manganese Dioxide	Oxygen (cathode reactant)
Aqueous solution of potassium hydroxide	Aqueous solution of potassium hydroxide or sodium hydroxide	Aqueous solution of potassium hydroxide or sodium hydroxide	A solvent solution of lithium perchlorate	30% potassium hydroxide
Rechargeable	Primary	Primary	Primary	Primary
Yes	No	No	No	No
300-2000	—	—	—	—
$Cd + 2NiOOH + 2H_2O \overset{KOH}{\rightleftharpoons} Cd(OH)_2 + 2Ni(OH)_2$	$Zn + 2MnO_2 \overset{KOH}{\underset{NaOH}{\rightarrow}}$ $ZnO + Mn_2O_3$	$Zn + Ag_2O \overset{KOH}{\underset{NaOH}{\rightarrow}}$ $ZnO + 2Ag$	$Li + MnO_2 \rightarrow LiMnO_2$	$Zn + \frac{1}{2}O_2 + H_2O \rightarrow Zn(OH)_2$
20mAh to 4Ah	16mAh to 28Ah	35mAh to 210mAh	70mAh to 200mAh	70mAH to 400mAH
12-16 1.2-1.5	50 8	50 8	15-30 2-3.5	150 15
Yes 8-10A	Yes No	Yes No	Yes No	Yes No
Flat	Flat	Flat	Flat	Flat
$-40°F(-40°C)$ to $140°F(60°C)$ $-4°F(-20°C)$ to $113°F(45°C)$	$-40°F(-40°C)$ to $140°F(60°C)$ $32°F(0°C)$ to $130°F(54.4°C)$	$-40°F(-40°C)$ to $140°F(60°C)$ $32°F(0°C)$ to $130°F(54.4°C)$	$-40°F(-40°C)$ to $140°F(60°C)$ $-4°F(-20°C)$ to $140°F(60°C)$	$32°F(0°C)$ to $104°F(40°C)$ $32°F(0°C)$ to $104°F(40°C)$
Very good at low temperature. Poor at high temperature.	Good at high temperature. Poor at low temperature.	Poor at low temperature.	Fair at low temperature.	Better at higher temperature.
Very Low	Low	Low	Low	Low
Low	Very Low	Very Low	Low	Self venting — low gassing.
Good	Good	Good	Good	Good
Low	High	High	High	Moderate
Excellent cycle life. Flat voltage discharge curves. Good high and low temperature performance, resistant to shock and vibration. Store indefinitely at any charge.	High service capacity to volume ratio. Flat voltage discharge curve. Good high-temperature performance.	Moderately flat voltage discharge curve	Higher voltage than other button cells. High energy density. Suitable for heavy drain uses (pulse discharge). Good storage life.	Flat discharge curve, lightweight — small size. 50% lighter than Mercuric Oxide cell. High energy density. Excellent storage life.
Initial cost high. Fair charge retention.	Poor low-temperature operating characteristics.	Limited to 1.5 volt applications.	Limited to 3 volt applications.	Requires atmospheric oxygen to activate the cell.

Chapter 4

TESTING AND REVITALIZING BATTERIES

The capacity of a battery is like the capacity of the gas tank in your car, but with one big difference. Your fuel tank has a gauge to tell you how much gas is in your tank. With batteries, there is no such gauge. There is no such tester. So we can't know how much capacity remains without unloading the battery.

A battery used twelve hours a day will have quite a different service capacity than the same battery used only two hours a day. There is also no correlation between continuous duty service and intermittent service. It is not possible to rate the capacity of a battery for intermittent service based on continuous duty testing.

Service capacity cannot be determined by amperage readings alone. If you were to compare a photoflash battery with a flashlight cell of the same size, it might appear that they have the same service capacity. The photoflash battery will deliver twice the amperage of the flashlight battery, but will have much less service capacity when used continually in flashlight use.

The condition of dry cell batteries should be tested under load with a voltmeter. The voltmeter will not determine remaining capacity, but you can if you know the battery's history. By comparing the voltmeter reading to capacity versus voltage data that's based on other batteries tested in similar service, you can estimate remaining capacity.

Testing a battery under load is the best way to check the battery. An open-circuit voltmeter reading on a battery gives no indication of the internal resistance or its ability to deliver current under load. A short circuit amperage reading can damage a battery and shorten its life. *Table E* presents the suggested testing loads for the most common batteries for typical applications. Compare the battery voltage reading while tested under load to the battery label voltage to determine the present battery condition for further use.

Percentage of Label Voltage	Battery Condition
0 - 61%	replace
62 - 72%	weak
73 - 105%	good

Table E. Battery Testing

Application	Battery Size	Ohms Load
Penlites	AAA	3.0
Toys, clocks, flashlights, movie cameras, cassette players	AA, C, D	2.25
Transistor, integrated circuit appliances	AA, C, D	10.0
Lantern	6 Volt	5.0
Solid-state radio Fire alarm Memory back-up supply	9 Volt	250
Photo flash	22.5 Volt	2000
Watches, calculators hearing aids	1.5 Volt Button	1500
Cameras	3.0 Volt Button	3000

BATTERY CHECKERS

Basically a battery checker is a miniature voltmeter that includes a fixed load resistor and is packaged to make it easy to use. It will measure the terminal voltage of a battery under fixed load. Several different checkers are available from Radio Shack *(Figure 4-1)*. A battery may have acceptable terminal voltage under a light load, but under a heavy load the terminal voltage may fall below acceptable cut-off voltage. This is due to high internal resistance created by use, or chemical degradation caused by prolonged shelf storage. In such cases, a battery checker may not show whether the battery can deliver higher current levels and still maintain terminal voltage.

BATTERY TESTERS

The Micronta® battery tester *(Figure 4-2)* measures terminal voltage under predetermined current loading for different size batteries. This measurement indicates the battery's true and accurate condition. As the chart shows, a Micronta battery tester has eight test ranges and is perfect for testing all Enercell batteries.

Select Voltage	Load Current	Replace/Good Voltage Indicated at:
1.5V (button)	1mA	1.125 ± 0.09V
1.5V (cylindrical)	150mA, 50mA	1.125 ± 0.09V
3.0V (Lithium)	1mA	2.250 ± 0.18V
6.0V	10mA	4.500 ± 0.36V
9.0V	10mA	6.750 ± 0.54V
12.0V	10mA	9.000 ± 0.72V
15.0V	10mA	11.250 ± 0.90V
22.5V	10mA	16.875 ± 1.35V

Figure 4-1. Battery Checker

Figure 4-2. Battery Tester

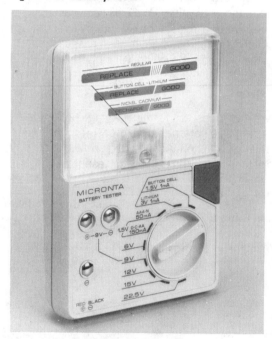

RECHARGING PRIMARY BATTERIES

Battery chargers have been around for a number of years. At best they attempt to rejuvenate primary batteries. Primary batteries are not designed nor intended to be recharged.

Carbon Zinc and Zinc Chloride batteries are rechargeable to some degree, provided the discharge and charge cycles are precisely controlled. The National Bureau of Standards (letter circular LC965) notes the following:

a) The discharge operating voltage should not be below 1.0 volt per cell if the battery is to be revitalized.

b) The battery should be recharged as soon as possible after removal from discharge service.

c) The ampere-hours of recharge should be 120 to 180 percent of the ampere-hours of discharge.

d) The charging current rate should be low enough to allow distribution of the recharge over a period of 12 to 16 hours.

e) Batteries should be placed in service immediately after rejuvenation because recharged batteries have poor storage life.

Chapter 5

THE TYPES OF BATTERIES

Carbon Zinc
GENERAL PURPOSE ENERCELL

Carbon Zinc, the work horse of batteries, has been used for years to power flashlights, portable radios, toys. Essentially it's the same as it was back in 1868 when it was developed by George Leclanche.

Carbon Zinc is the least expensive of batteries and available in all popular sizes. Use them, throw them away, replace them with new ones best characterize how these batteries are used.

Carbon Zinc batteries work best with low or moderate power requirements. With every use the voltage drops until it is time to throw it away. The Carbon Zinc is limited for use in some of the newer portable electronic products with their higher drain requirements, but is still good for flashlights and intermittent use.

General purpose batteries like Carbon Zinc don't withstand heat and cold very well. And long storage periods when temperatures soar above 100°F, such as in our cars during the summer, cause deterioration. The heat drives out the moisture from the chemical mix in the cell. It's not a good performer at low temperatures either. At 0°F or below, the cell's chemical activity is so decreased, that there is little service life. But Carbon Zinc batteries do have three big advantages: low cost, a wide number of sizes, and they are readily available.

TECHNICAL DETAILS

Construction: *Figure 5-1* is a typical Carbon Zinc, size D, cylindrical battery. The electrochemical system consists of a zinc can anode, a manganese-dioxide cathode, an electrolyte of ammonium chloride and zinc chloride in water. Powdered carbon is added to the depolarizing mix to improve conductivity as well as to hold moisture. The carbon electrode at the center serves to collect electrons from the cathode mix of manganese-dioxide.

Chemical Reaction: $2MnO_2 + 2NH_4Cl + Zn \rightarrow ZnCl_2 \cdot 2NH_3 + H_2O + Mn_2O_3$

Temperature: Storage $-40°F$ to $120°F$ ($-40°C$ to $48.9°C$)
Operating $-20°F$ to $130°F$ ($-6.7°C$ to $54.4°C$)

Low temperature drastically reduces service capacity.

Voltage Discharge Curve: Sloping.

Recharging: Carbon Zinc batteries are not designed to be recharged. They may be revitalized when partially discharged; recharging after a full discharge is not possible. For more details on revitalization see Chapter 4.

Internal Resistance: Very low; it increases with usage, storage or at low temperature.

Impedance: Low.

Figure 5-1. Cutaway View — Typical Carbon Zinc Battery

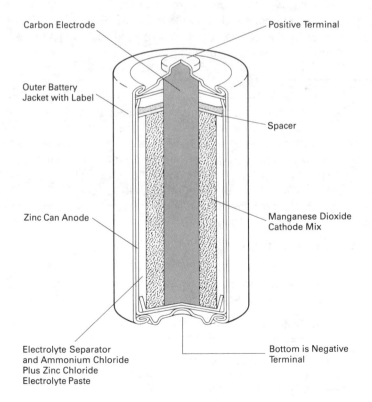

Carbon Electrode

Positive Terminal

Outer Battery
Jacket with Label

Spacer

Zinc Can Anode

Manganese Dioxide
Cathode Mix

Electrolyte Separator
and Ammonium Chloride
Plus Zinc Chloride
Electrolyte Paste

Bottom is Negative
Terminal

Zinc Chloride
HEAVY DUTY ENERCELL EXTRA LIFE

The Zinc Chloride battery is a beefed up version of the general purpose Carbon Zinc battery. Variation in the chemical mix increases its capacity fifty percent. This kind of capacity makes it a better choice than Carbon Zinc because it can deliver more current. Zinc Chloride batteries are superior to Carbon Zinc in leak resistance. Zinc Chloride batteries cost sixty percent more than Carbon Zinc. They are available everywhere and come in many sizes.

Voltage decreases with each use until cutoff voltage is reached and the battery becomes useless. While Zinc Chloride batteries are labeled heavy duty, they do not withstand high temperatures much better than Carbon Zinc; however, they do perform better at low temperatures. Storage, or shelf life, is much longer than Carbon Zinc batteries, but storing them at high temperatures will shorten their life dramatically.

The heavy duty Zinc Chloride battery is moderately priced for its service capacity. Comparing Zinc Chloride to Carbon Zinc: Zinc Chloride weighs twenty percent more, offers a fifty percent increase in service capacity, has the ability to sustain higher current drain and performs better at lower temperatures. If you use lots of Zinc Chloride batteries, but some stay idle for long periods, you should consider stepping up to Alkaline batteries.

TECHNICAL DETAILS

Construction: A zinc can anode, a manganese-dioxide cathode, a zinc chloride electrode, and a carbon electrode collect electrons from the cathode mix and are the key components of this battery. See *Figure 5-2.* The electrolyte is zinc chloride. It reduces electrode blocking caused by the reaction byproducts as well as electrode polarization at high current densities. This improved efficiency results in greater current output then Carbon Zinc batteries. Further, they will operate at greater current drain for a longer time with terminal voltage under load remaining higher then a comparable size Carbon Zinc battery.

Chemical Reaction:
$$8MnO_2 + 4Zn + ZnCl_2 + 9H_2O \rightarrow$$
$$8MnOOH + ZnCl_2 \cdot 4ZnO \cdot 5H_2O$$

Water in the cell is consumed by an oxide compound reaction, so the the cell is virtually dry at the end of its service life.

Temperature: Storage $-40°F$ to $160°F$ ($-40°C$ to $71.1°C$)
Operating $0°F$ to $160°F$ ($-17.8°C$ to $71.1°C$)

A Zinc Chloride battery will withstand higher storage temperatures than Carbon Zinc. It can also be used at both higher and lower temperatures because of its greater electrode efficiency.

Voltage Discharge Curve: Sloping, does not fall off to as great a degree as Carbon Zinc, especially under higher current drain.

Recharging: The Zinc Chloride battery is a primary battery and is not designed to be recharged. It may be revitalized with a charger if it is partially discharged. See Chapter 4 for more details on revitalizing batteries.

Internal Resistance: Very low, increases with usage, storage, or at low temperature.

Impedance: Low

Figure 5-2. Cutaway View — Typical Zinc Chloride Battery

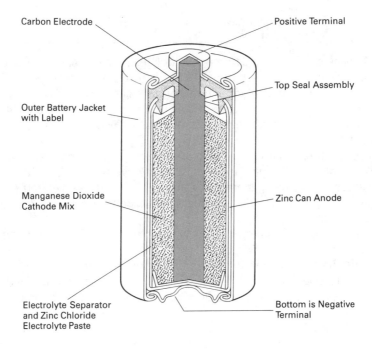

Carbon Electrode

Positive Terminal

Top Seal Assembly

Outer Battery Jacket
with Label

Manganese Dioxide
Cathode Mix

Zinc Can Anode

Electrolyte Separator
and Zinc Chloride
Electrolyte Paste

Bottom is Negative
Terminal

Alkaline Manganese Dioxide
ALKALINE ENERCELL

The Alkaline battery offers real improvements for consumers. It offers higher energy capacity, better high and low temperature performance, and longer term storage. Since its introduction about twenty years ago it has continued to drop in price as manufacturing volume increased. Although an Alkaline battery may cost two to three times more than that of a Carbon Zinc or Zinc Chloride battery, it will out perform both, four to six, even ten times, depending on the use.

Alkaline batteries are perfect for products with high current demand such as cassette recorders, camera flash units, flashlights, battery driven toys, and electronic games. Compare the performance of an Alkaline battery to Carbon Zinc in the following:

	Alkaline % of Carbon Zinc
Flashlight	800
Radio	350
Portable TV	800
Tape Recorders/Players	450
Motor Driven Toys	750

An Alkaline battery has a different electrolyte chemistry and is constructed differently than a Carbon Zinc battery. It's this difference that provides the higher electrochemical efficiency, which in turn influences its increased capacity, longer storage life, and better performance at both high and low temperatures. And, although its voltage does fall a little bit every time it's used, it is not as steep a slope as Carbon Zinc.

Alkaline batteries may be stored for two years at room temperature and still hold 90 percent of their original electrical capacity, even 80 percent after four years. Because of their long storage life and ability to withstand extreme temperatures, Alkaline batteries are ideal for emergency flashlights, especially in homes and in cars.

The Alkaline battery is half again as heavy as a Carbon Zinc battery, but it has to be to store all that extra energy.

In short, the Alkaline battery costs more but gives more; more use and more storage life. It's also better whenever the product demands high current drain. Alkaline is head and shoulders over Zinc Chloride and a giant over Carbon Zinc.

TECHNICAL DETAILS

Construction: *Figure 5-3* shows a typical size-D Alkaline battery. They are available in both cylindrical and button configurations. The electrochemical system consists of an anode that is a gelled mixture of amalgamated zinc powder and potassium hydroxide electrolyte. The cathode is a mixture of high purity electrolytic manganese-dioxide and carbon. A special nonwoven separator prevents solid particles from migrating in the cell and brass sheet metal anode collector are housed in an inner steel can which serves as the cathode. The three-way electrochemical reaction takes place between the high purity, high density conductive carbon matrix cathode, the large surface area of amalgamated zinc, and the highly conductive electrolytic solution.

Chemical Reaction: $2Zn + 3MnO_2 \overset{KOH}{\rightarrow} 2ZnO + Mn_3O_4$.

Temperature: Storage $\quad -40°F$ to $120°F$ ($-40°C$ to $48.9°C$)
Operating $-20°F$ to $130°F$ ($-28.9°C$ to $54.4°C$)

Voltage Discharge Curve: Sloping, but much less than that of Carbon Zinc batteries or Zinc Chloride. Alkaline batteries are best suited for continuous or high current loads.

Recharging: Alkaline batteries are primary type and are not intended to be recharged. Attempting to recharge an Alkaline battery could cause it to explode.

Internal Resistance: Very low; remains almost constant until the end of its life when it will increase rapidly.

Impedance: Very low, much less than Carbon Zinc.

Figure 5-3. Cutaway View — Typical Alkaline Battery

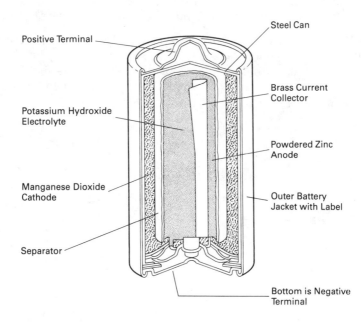

Steel Can

Positive Terminal

Brass Current Collector

Potassium Hydroxide Electrolyte

Powdered Zinc Anode

Manganese Dioxide Cathode

Outer Battery Jacket with Label

Separator

Bottom is Negative Terminal

Mercuric Oxide Batteries
ENERCELL WATCH, CALCULATOR, HEARING AID BATTERIES

For an application that requires a high energy density and a flat voltage curve, the Mercuric Oxide battery is the answer. Typical applications are hearing aids, watches, calculators, electronic cameras, and electronic measuring instruments. For the power and value they deliver, these button wonders are modestly priced. Two types of Mercuric Oxide batteries are available. One type, with a sodium hydroxide electrolyte, has a near constant voltage at low current drain. It is ideal for electronic watches, calculators and hearing aids. The other type with a potassium hydroxide electrolyte provides near constant voltage at higher current drains. This meets the high pulse current demands in electronic cameras with flash, and watches with back lighting. Cells with a mercuric oxide cathode system are particularly useful where greater terminal voltage stability is needed.

TECHNICAL DETAILS

Construction: Mercuric Oxide batteries are produced in cylindrical and button construction. Both have the same electrochemical systems, but case designs are different. The internal electrodes may be either flat or cylindrical (See *Figure 5-4*). Mercuric Oxide cells have a cathode of mercuric oxide (HgO) or mercuric oxide/manganese dioxide (HgO/MnO_2). The anode is pure amalgamated zinc with a concentrated electrolyte of potassium or sodium hydroxide. The electrolyte is absorbed on a multi-layer separator system. Operational characteristics will differ depending upon which cathode or electrolyte chemical is used.

Current Delivery: Current delivery is determined by the type of electrolyte. The potassium hydroxide (KOH) electrolyte offers less resistance to current flow, especially at heavier current loads. It also allows the cell to operate at a greater efficiency than the sodium hydroxide (NaOH) electrolyte. *Figure 5-6* shows this efficiency difference.

Chemical Reaction: The chemical reaction during discharge for a Mercuric Oxide cell with a mercuric oxide/manganese dioxide (HgO/MnO_2) cathode and potassium hydroxide (KOH) electrolyte is:

$$Zn + 2MnO_2 \xrightarrow{KOH} ZnO + Mn_2O_3$$

Temperature: Storage $-40°F$ to $140°F$ ($-40°C$ to $60°C$)
             Operating $32°F$ to $130°F$ ($0°C$ to $54.4°C$)

Mercuric Oxide batteries with a potassium hydroxide (KOH) electrolyte will operate at low temperatures with less loss in efficiency than those with a sodium hydroxide (NaOH) electrolyte.

Voltage Discharge Curve: A Mercuric Oxide cell with a mercuric oxide cathode will have an open circuit voltage of 1.35 volts and a very flat voltage discharge curve. This cathode chemical construction is used in cells for watches, photographic meters and as a reference voltage standard in measurement instruments. A Mercuric Oxide cell with a mixed mercuric oxide/manganese dioxide cathode will have an open circuit voltage of 1.4 volts and a more sloping voltage discharge curve. Cells with this construction often are used for hearing aids and electronic measurement instruments. A comparison of the two cathode systems is shown in *Figure 5-5.*

Recharging: Mercuric Oxide batteries are designed and intended for primary battery use only. *CAUTION: Don't attempt to recharge a Mercuric Oxide battery; it could explode.*

Impedance: Very low.

Figure 5-4. Cutaway View — Typical Mercuric Oxide Button Battery

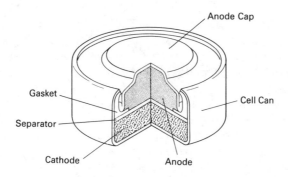

Figure 5-5. Typical Voltage Discharge Curves   **Figure 5-6. Current Drain Efficiency**

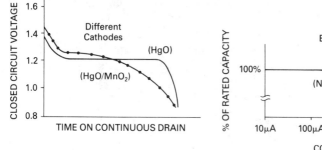

Silver Oxide Batteries
ENERCELL WATCH AND CALCULATOR BATTERIES

Silver Oxide is the nickname for a silver oxide-alkaline-zinc primary battery. And it's nicely priced for the dependability and power it delivers.

Two types of Silver Oxide batteries are available. One type with a sodium hydroxide (NaOH) electrolyte and the other with a potassium hydroxide (KOH) electrolyte. Sodium hydroxide types last two to three years making them highly suitable for quartz analog watches or digital watches without backlights. Potassium hydroxide types are better for the short bursts of higher current drains that are required from LCD watches with backlights. Hearing aids and electronic measuring instruments also use batteries with a potassium hydroxide electrolyte in combination with a special separator to match the application.

The Silver Oxide battery has a higher closed circuit voltage than a Mercuric Oxide battery and a flatter voltage discharge curve than the Alkaline Manganese Dioxide battery.

Technical Details

Construction: Silver Oxide batteries have flat circular cathodes and homogeneous gelled anodes. A cutaway view of a silver oxide-alkaline-zinc miniature round cell is shown in *Figure 5-7*. The cathodes are a mixture of silver oxide with a trace of manganese dioxide. The anode is a gelled mixture of amalgamated zinc. The electrolyte is highly alkaline sodium hydroxide (NaOH) or potassium hydroxide (KOH). The electrolyte is integrated into the anode gel. A special separator prevents any migration of solid particles. Performance and efficiency depends upon which hydroxide electrolyte is used.

There are also Silver Oxide hybrid cells. They use a potassium hydroxide electrolyte (KOH) with a greater mix of manganese dioxide and reduced silver oxide in the cathode. The reduced silver oxide results in a service life reduction with a sloping operating voltage discharge curve. These hybrid cells are used in low current drain applications.

Current Delivery: The current delivery capabilities of a Silver Oxide cell are determined by the type of electrolyte used as shown in *Figure 5-8*. Like the Mercuric Oxide cell, when the potassium electrolyte is used, the cell offers less resistance to current flow. This allows the cell to operate at a higher efficiency under heavier current drains. At low current drains, both the sodium hydroxide (NaOH) and potassium hydroxide (KOH) electrolyte operate with the same efficiency.

Chemical Reaction: The chemical reaction during discharge for a silver oxide-alkaline-zinc primary cell with a potassium hydroxide electrolyte is:

$$Zn + Ag_2O \xrightarrow{KOH} ZnO + 2Ag$$

Temperature: Storage   −40°F to 150°F (−40°C to 60°C)
                  Operating   32°F to 130°F (0°C to 54.4°C)

These temperature ranges are the same as Mercuric Oxide batteries. Like the Mercuric Oxide batteries with the potassium hydroxide (KOH) electrolyte, the Silver Oxide operates with less loss in efficiency at low temperatures than cells with sodium hydroxide (NaOH) electrolyte.

Voltage Discharge Curve: Open circuit voltage is 1.6 volts. With current drain it is typically 1.5 volts or more. Silver Oxide cells exhibit a very flat operating voltage discharge curve that has a higher voltage than Mercuric Oxide cells. A comparison is shown in *Figure 5-9.*

Recharging: The Silver Oxide battery is designed and intended for primary battery use only. *CAUTION: Attempts to recharge a Silver Oxide battery can cause the cell to explode.*

Impedance: Low.

Figure 5-7. Cutaway View — Typical Silver Oxide Button Battery

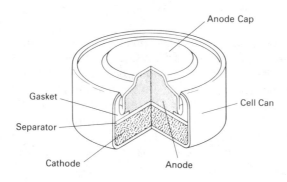

Figure 5.8. Current Drain Efficiency

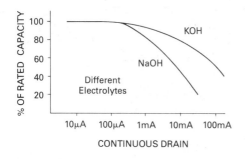

Figure 5-9. Typical Voltage Discharge Curve

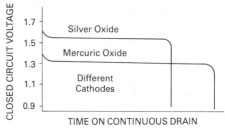

Lithium Manganese Dioxide Battery
LITHIUM ENERCELL

Here is a battery that meets the requirements of new electronic circuit technologies. Characterized by high energy density, high power density, good storage life and discharge performance, they offer a big advantage over Alkaline batteries. And their cost is modest.

Lithium primary batteries are available in a wide variety of electrochemical and physical configurations. They find use in cardiac pacemakers, in CMOS (complimentary metal-oxide-semiconductor) memory storage, powering LCDs in watches, calculators, and in other military and medical applications.

Their dependability and usefulness rests squarely on solid performance. Because of lithium manganese oxide's stability, they can be stored for several years. Operating temperatures have little effect on operating characteristics because the cell is so efficient. Lithium batteries offer twice the voltage of other button cell batteries. And their small size, lightweight, and high energy density make them perfect for applications that require high drain or pulse discharge over a broad temperature range. They also provide excellent performance at low temperatures. Also, storage life is outstanding because their self discharge is so very low.

Battery technologists have long been aware that lithium has the highest potential on the emf-scale as well as a low equivalent weight. This makes it a very good anode candidate for a high-energy high-density battery. Only recently has a manufacturing process been developed to electroplate lithium for use as an anode. This breakthrough made the battery a commercial product.

The Lithium battery voltage is 3.0 volts; the voltage discharge curve is flat. They are available in both cylindrical and button shapes; buttons being most common (See *Figure 5-10*). The service capacity of a Lithium Enercell button batteries range from 70 to 200 mAh.

TECHNICAL DETAILS

Construction: The electrochemical system consists of a cathode which is a mixture of manganese dioxide, a carbon black conducting agent, and a binder. The electrolyte is a solvent solution of lithium perchlorate ($LiClO_4$) in propylene carbonate. Its water content is below 50-ppm (parts per million). The anode is made of lithium foil pressed into a stainless steel anode can. Lithium batteries are assembled in a high purity argon atmosphere.

Chemical Reaction: The discharge mechanism of a Lithium Manganese Dioxide battery occurs because lithium ions diffuse into the manganese dioxide's crystal lattice. This reduces tetravalent manganese to trivalent manganese.

$$Li + MnO_2 \rightarrow LiMnO_2$$

Temperature: Storage and Operating − 40°F to 140°F (− 40°C to 60°C)

Voltage Discharge Curve: Very flat.

Recharging: Lithium Manganese Dioxide batteries are designated primary batteries and are not designed to be recharged. *CAUTION: Do not attempt to recharge the battery; it could cause the cell to explode.*

Internal Resistance: Low and remains stable throughout its life.

Impedance: Low and remains constant.

Figure 5-10. Cutaway View — Typical Lithium Manganese Dioxide Round Battery

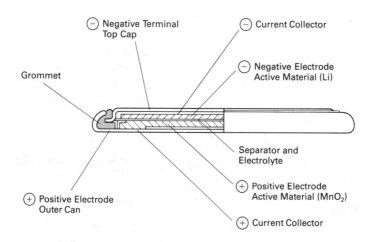

Zinc Air Batteries
ENERCELL PAGER/HEARING AID BATTERIES

The Zinc Air battery, like its Lithium cousin, comes out of the latest space age technology. Specifically, research on fuel cells led to design refinements on an air electrode, which led to the Zinc Air battery.

This battery actually uses the oxygen in the air for its cathode reactant. A tiny access hole, sealed with plastic tape keeps it dormant, and storage life is excellent too. Simply remove the tape and the battery is ready to use.

A Zinc Air battery has 40 percent more energy than a Lithium battery of the same size. It has twice the capacity of Silver Oxide. It also weighs about a third less than the same size Silver Oxide battery. Long storage life, very flat voltage discharge curve, and lightweight make it ideal for hearing aids, pagers, and personal medical instruments. Zinc Air batteries work best in a relative humidity range of 25 to 80 percent and in a temperature range between 32°F through 104°F. Once their seal is broken and it's activated, the battery's capacity should be used within sixty days.

TECHNICAL DETAILS

Construction: The Zinc Air button cell consists of an anode and cathode subassembly held together by a crimp seal on the cathode can. A cross section view of a Zinc Air button cell is shown in *Figure 5-11*. The major components are:

Negative terminal can made from tri-clad material.

Positive can of nickel plated steel.

Nylon insulator separating the electrodes.

Sealant to reduce electrolyte creep.

Anode slurry consisting of zinc powder and 30% by weight potassium hydroxide.

Air distribution membrane.

Air cathode.

Separating membranes which allow ionic conductance.

The air electrode is 0.5mm thick and is not consumed during discharge. The reaction at the negative terminal is very efficient due to the high surface area of the zinc powder. The zinc hydroxide reaction product [$Zn(OH)_2$] solubility in the potassium hydroxide (KOH) decreases at 0°C and below. The reaction at the positive terminal can involve a two electron electrochemical reduction of oxygen (O_2) to a perhydroxide specie (OH −) which subsequently disproportionates to hydroxide and oxygen. Because the atmosphere provides an unlimited supply of oxygen, the zinc mass is the controlling factor in the cells available capacity.

Once the cell is activated, the voltage stabilizes between 1.4 and 1.45 volts. Drawing discharge current quickly lowers the voltage to 1.3 volts or less. Drain currents greater than 50% of the rated limiting current lessens the batteries capacity. Drains less than 50% of the limiting current allows efficient discharge of the cell.

Chemical Reaction: $Zn + \frac{1}{2}O_2 + H_2O \rightarrow Zn(OH)_2$

Temperature: Storage and Operating 32°F to 104°F (0°C to 40°C)

Voltage Discharge Curve: Depends on current drain, but relatively flat during a discharge range of 1.3 to 1.1 volts. At the end of life, voltage drops off rapidly exhibiting a knee in the discharge curve. Very little capacity remains after the voltage drops below 1.0 volts.

Recharging: Zinc Air cells are designed and intended for primary use only. *CAUTION: Attempts to recharge could cause an unsafe condition due to the expulsion of cell chemical mix.*

Impedance: Low.

Figure 5-11. Cross Section View — Typical Zinc Air Button Battery

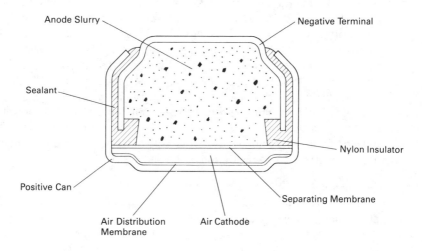

Nickel-Cadmium Batteries
RECHARGEABLE ENERCELL AND RECHARGEABLE HI-CAPACITY

The Nickel-Cadmium battery may well be today's best battery buy. It's big benefit is that it may be charged and recharged many times. Primary batteries are used once and thrown away. Nickel-Cadmium rechargeable batteries may replace most primary batteries. Although "Ni-Cds" are initially expensive, they are more often than not the cheapest power source in the long run.

The principle behind their rechargeability is simple. Oxidation which occurs at the negative electrode equals the oxidation reduction at the positive electrode. This action generates power. In a rechargeable battery, both electrode reactions are reversible. An external input forces the discharge reaction in reverse. In effect, it is recharged.

Nickel-Cadmium batteries may be stored either charged or discharged. If stored charged, a Ni-Cd will discharge at a rate of two percent per day at 68°F (20°C). If it is stored, but not on a trickle charge, it is recommended that they be charged every sixty days. Also, it's not wise to store Ni-Cds under load; for example, a flashlight with the switch on. Such a continuous load on a discharged battery may cause it to leak.

There also is a phenomenon associated with a Nickel-Cadmium battery worth noting. It can form a memory. The likelihood of this happening in a normal consumer application is not high, but one never knows. Memory forms when a repetitive cycle is inadvertently created. One way it happens is by successively causing a partial discharge which results in a subsequent partial charge. When this occurs, the normal battery capacity is not usable at normal voltage levels. The memory effect can be corrected by fully discharging the battery and then merely charging it fully at the recommended charge rate. This may have to be repeated several times to completely remove the partial memory.

Enercell rechargeable batteries range in service capacities from 80 mAh for the 9V rectangular battery to 4.0 Ah for the size D Rechargeable Hi-Capacity battery. Some Nickel-Cadmium batteries have about half the service capacity of the same size Alkaline battery, but are 20 to 30 percent lighter in weight. The Rechargeable Hi-Capacity Enercell batteries have more service capacity than the regular Rechargeable Enercell batteries of the same size.

TECHNICAL DETAILS

Construction: Nickel-Cadmium batteries come in cylindrical and rectangular shapes (See *Figure 5-12*). The nickel-plated steel case is the negative terminal. The cell cover is the positive terminal; it also contains the venting mechanism. The positive and negative plates are isolated from each other by a porous separator. Both plates and separators are wound into a compact roll inside the case. Uncharged, the positive electrode is nickelous hydroxide [$Ni(OH)_2$]. The negative electrode is cadmium hydroxide [$Cd(OH)_2$]. When charged, the positive electrode is nickelic hydroxide (NiOOH) and the negative electrode is metallic cadmium (Cd). The electrolyte is potassium hydroxide (KOH). Toward the end of a charge cycle and during overcharge, oxygen is generated at the positive nickel electrode and hydrogen could be formed at the negative cadmium electrode. However, the sealed cells are designed to operate at low internal gas pressure. Cell design is such that the cadmium electrode has excess capacity. During charge, the positive nickel electrode reaches full charge first and starts oxygen generation. Since the negative cadmium electrode will not reach full charge, hydrogen is not generated. The internal cell structure allows the oxygen to migrate to the negative cadmium electrode where is directly oxidizes. Since hydrogen is not generated, the oxygen reaches the active surface area of the cadmium plate and is removed from the gas phase. The oxygen acts like an internal chemical short circuit allowing the Nickel-Cadmium cell to be continuously overcharged without developing high internal gas pressure.

Figure 5-12. Cutaway View — Typical Nickel-Cadmium Battery

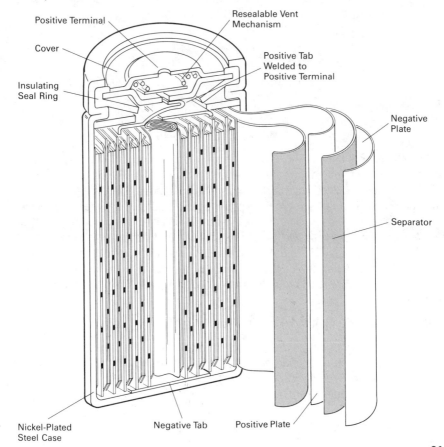

Positive Terminal

Resealable Vent Mechanism

Cover

Positive Tab Welded to Positive Terminal

Insulating Seal Ring

Negative Plate

Separator

Nickel-Plated Steel Case

Negative Tab

Positive Plate

Nickel-Cadmium batteries are available in two types: vented cells and hermetically sealed cells. Vented cells must be properly positioned so they will vent properly. They also require water for maintenance. Vented cells are used in commercial and military applications. Hermetically sealed rechargeable batteries, on the other hand, are maintenance free. They may be used in any position and may be discharged-charged many times. Most sealed Nickel-Cadmium batteries have venting mechanisms which operate should the cell's internal pressure increase to the range of 150 to 300 psig. The internal cell pressure will remain well below the setting to operate the vent if the cell is charged and discharged properly.

There are two types of vent mechanisms used in sealed Nickel-Cadmium batteries. The first vent type is the "one-shot." The vent opens at the preset pressure and then remains open. Although the cell still operates after a "one-shot" seal has opened, its life is curtailed as the cell drys out. The second type is a resealable safety vent that opens when the internal pressure reaches the preset value and recloses as the internal pressure is relieved. As the resealable vent operates, gas is vented. When conditions return to normal, the vent closes and the cell reseals hermetically.

Chemical Reaction:

$$Cd + 2NiOOH + 2H_2O \underset{\text{Charged}}{\overset{\text{Discharged}}{\underset{KOH}{\rightleftarrows}}} Cd(OH)_2 + 2Ni(OH)_2$$

Temperature: Discharge $\quad -4°F$ to $113°F$ ($-20°C$ to $45°C$)

Storage $\quad\quad -40°F$ to $140°F$ ($-40°C$ to $60°C$)

Charging $\quad\quad 32°F$ to $113°F$ ($0°C$ to $45°C$)

Voltage Discharge Curve: The Nickel-Cadmium battery open circuit voltage is 1.2 volts. Compare this to a primary battery cell voltage of 1.5 volts, e.g., Carbon Zinc, Zinc Chloride, Alkaline. Standard primary batteries have a sloping discharge voltage curve. The terminal voltage starts at 1.5 volts, but declines shortly to 1.2 volts. It will continue to decrease as the battery is used to a point (approximately 0.9V) where the cell must be discarded. The Nickel-Cadmium voltage discharge curve is flat. As a result, the cell will deliver 1.2 volts throughout most of the discharge time. When the current capacity is depleted, the voltage decreases and the cell must be recharged. Most of the current capacity is above 1.0 volts per cell.

Internal Resistance: Quite low, in the milliohm range.

Impedance: Cell impedance depends on frequency and state of charge. Impedance is lower for a charged cell than a discharged cell. In either state the cells have a high effective capacitance. Their impedance is quite low and they make excellent ripple filters, especialy when they are being continuously overcharged.

Charging Nickel-Cadmium Batteries: The letter C is used to indicate discharge or charge rate. Both rates are equal to the rated ampere-hour capacity of the battery. For example, the one hour charge current rate for a 2.0 Ah battery is 2.0 amperes (C = 2.0); the 10 hour rate is C/10 which is equal to 2.0/10 = 0.2 amperes. The discharge current may also be represented as a proportion of the C-rate. Example: the one-tenth discharge rate would be 0.1C. The rated capacity of a rechargeable battery is a function of the discharge C-rate. The lower the discharge C-rate, the greater the rated capacity.

Constant current charging is recommended for sealed Nickel-Cadmium batteries. It is necessary to replace 140% of the capacity (ampere-hours) removed from the battery during discharge. This 40% overcharge is due to the charge acceptance efficiencies of the cell. Follow these guidelines for the three types of charges:

Trickle Charge maintains a full charged battery for standby service. Use the 30 to 50 hour rate.

Normal Charge means to charge and hold at a full charge with little cell degradation. Use the 10 to 30 hour rate.

Fast Charge use high charge with caution. Some cells will accept a fast charge without damage. Use the 3 to 10 hour rate.

When charging consumer type Nickel-Cadmium batteries don't exceed the 10 hour charge rate. Various Archer Nickel-Cadmium battery chargers are available from Radio Shack. See Chapter 6 for more information on ready-to-use chargers. Custom constant current chargers can be made for special products or custom applications. Here are some basic types (*Figures 5-13* and *5-14*).

| **Figure 5-13. Half-Wave Charger** | **Figure 5-14. Full-Wave Charger** |

Half-Wave Rectifier

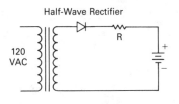

Full-Wave Bridge Rectifier

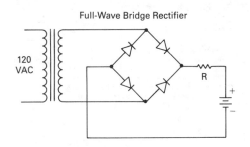

Chapter 6

NICKEL-CADMIUM BATTERY CHARGERS

Radio Shack offers ten types of Archer constant-current Ni-Cd battery chargers. Each delivers the proper ten-hour rate (C/10) charging current. Each is especially designed to safely charge Enercell Nickel-Cadmium batteries. Because of their charging characteristics at the C/10 rate, Ni-Cds require 14 to 16 hours charge time to become fully recharged. Current outputs from an Archer charger are such that overcharging is not harmful to the Ni-Cd battery. The batteries may be safely left on continuous charge. Data on the available chargers is as follows:

Table F. Archer Nickel-Cadmium Battery Changers

Radio Shack Catalog Number	Number of Battery Positions		Charging Currents* in Milliamperes for Battery Size					
	Cylindrical	9V Rect	D	C	AA	AAA	N	9V
23-131	—	1	—	—	—	—	—	8mA
23-132	4	2	120mA	120mA	50mA	†	††	8mA
23-133	4	—	—	—	50mA	—	—	—
23-134	10	—	120mA	120mA	50mA	†	††	—
23-136	6	—	—	—	50mA	15mA	—	—
23-142**	4	—	400mA	180mA	—	—	—	—
23-231***								
23-232 (12V DC Source)***								
23-233****	6	2	350mA	350mA	155mA	55mA	—	22mA
23-234*****	4	—	—	350mA	—	—	—	—

* Nominal current @ 120VAC 60Hz input.
** High capacity charger for use only with Enercell Rechargeable Hi-Capacity® batteries.
† With assessory module 23-135
†† With accessory module 23-137
*** For charging 23-230 radio controlled racing battery pack
**** Quick charger – charges in 5 hrs. or less
***** Quick charger – charges in 2 hrs.

A standard and deluxe charger are shown in *Figure 6-1*. Cylindrical batteries (D, C, AA) are charged in pairs. The nine-volt rectangular battery may be charged singularly. AAA and N cells may be charged using an adapter module. Be careful when inserting cylindrical batteries into the charger; make sure that the battery polarity corresponds to what is embossed in the charger chamber. Cylindrical batteries should be positioned in the bottom of the battery holder chamber to assure good connection to the proper contacts.

The Enercell Rechargeable Hi-Capacity® batteries have increased capacity over the standard Enercell Rechargeable Nickel-Cadmium batteries. The high-capacity charger (23-142) is designed for the increased capacity to match the C/10 charge rate. The regular (low capacity) Rechargeable Enercell batteries *should not* be charged in the high-capacity charger.

As mentioned, an accessory module that holds AAA and N batteries is available that adapts to the existing battery pockets. This adapter charger module will fit into some chargers, but not all. If the charger module for AAA and N Ni-Cds are placed into a charger chamber, it is recommended that, for a full charge, the AAA and N sizes be left on charge for 16 hours. They should not be left in the charger for a continuous trickle charge. The LED chamber light indicator will not light up when charging a size AAA or N cell with the adapter in a chamber slot.

Follow the instructions carefully when using the charger. The instructions should always be stored with the charger so they are available for ready reference.

Figure 6-1. Nickel-Cadmium Battery Charger

a. Standard   a. Deluxe

Quick-Charge Chargers

Figure 6-2 shows a quick-charge charger for Nickel-Cadmium batteries. Many Nickel-Cadmium batteries can accept being charged at a quick-charge rate. *Table F* shows the quick-charge currents compared to normal charging currents. Charging time is reduced from 14 to 16 hours to 5 to 6 hours. The 23-234 charger charges Ni-Cd batteries in 2 hours. If you want to measure charging current, the following describes a temporary method using a battery charger as the source.

Figure 6-2. Quick Charger

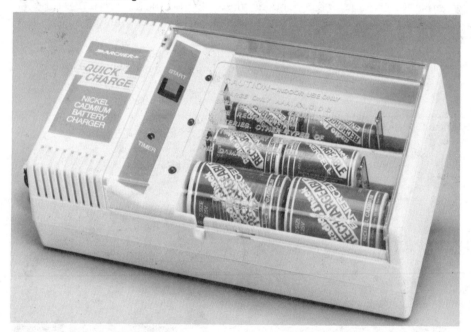

TESTING CHARGING CURRENT

First, you must have a meter with the proper amperage scale and capacity to measure the charging current. *Table F* lists the range of charging currents for different batteries in various chargers. The accuracy of the current measurements is determined by the meter used.

The internal resistance of the meter reduces the charging current because it is in series with the charger power supply and the charging battery. An auto-range multi-tester, such as Radio Shack 22-193, has an internal resistance of about 2 ohms on the 200mA scale. A VOM, such as Radio Shack 22-201A, has an internal resistance of about 1 ohm on the 250mA scale. Any meter resistance reduces the initial charging current by about 5 to 10% when charging two 1.5V cylindrical cells in series with 120mA.

Second, you must be able to get the ammeter into the charging circuit so it is in series with the battery. This may be easily accomplished for cylindrical cells by using a temporary method as follows:

1. Cut a piece of vinyl electrical tape about four (4) inches long.
2. Lay the tape flat with the adhesive side up.
3. Cut two pieces of aluminum foil to the width of the electrical tape and each three (3) inches long.
4. Align the foil strips on the electrical tape leaving a 1/4" – 1/2" space in the center of the tape. The foil should extend about an inch from each end of the tape.
5. Fold the electrical tape with the aluminum foil to the outside.
6. Unplug the battery charger.
7. Insert the fold of the folded assembly between the negative end of the battery and the contact tang of the battery charger.
8. Separate the two pieces of foil so they don't contact each other. The two pieces of foil are the terminals to which you will connect the ammeter.
9. Connect the positive lead of the meter to the foil strip which contacts the battery.
10. Connect the negative lead to the foil which contacts the charger tang. You now have inserted the ammeter in series with the charger circuit.
11. Plug in the charger and read the charging current on the ammeter.

Chapter 7

GUIDELINES AND SPECIFICATIONS FOR DESIGNERS

DESIGN GUIDELINES

1. Keep in mind that a customer seldom evaluates anything beyond service life. Select a good balance between service life, size for best performance, and customer satisfaction.
2. Choose a battery that is sold everywhere. The Enercell batteries listed in this guidebook are available at Radio Shack stores.
3. Battery compartments should be vented so the battery can breathe. Allow for the battery to expand and contract. Don't pot or encapsulate a battery.
4. Designers of watertight or airtight devices should provide for evolution of hydrogen from the battery. The hydrogen must be absorbed or vented and not be allowed to mix with air or oxygen in the products. A combination of gas, high temperature, or electrical discharge can ignite the gas causing fire or explosion.
5. If there is a heat source near the battery be sure to design the equipment so the heat source is located away from the battery, or provide for proper cooling. Customers can quickly become dissatisfied with the product, the battery, or both, if they feel service life is too short.
6. Connect batteries in series. A reversal of battery polarity in a parallel circuit causes the battery to be in a charge condition. This loads other cells and can cause the reversed battery to leak or rupture.
7. Specify spring brass, beryllium copper or plated steel with nickel, silver or gold flashing for the battery contact design.
8. If the battery has a metal jacket, be sure it is properly isolated from other circuit components to prevent a short circuit.
9. Battery compartments should be designed to protect the device against battery leakage. Leakage sometimes will occur in certain rare conditions or because of customer neglect or abuse.
10. Battery compartments should be designed for easy access, yet be tamper proof for child protection.

11. Use American National Standards Institute dimensional standards for battery compartment design.
12. It is adviseable to design the product power circuit to disconnect from the battery when the terminal voltage reaches the lowest functional voltage value. Don't allow the circuit to continue to load the battery after cutoff voltage is reached. Continued battery drain after cutoff voltage may cause leakage and cell rupture.
13. Using an ac adapter usually will extend service life. Design the ac adapter connection so that the primary battery will be disconnected from the circuit when the ac adapter is connected. This prevents a primary battery from being recharged, which could result in leakage or rupture.

POINTS YOU SHOULD MAKE WITH THE CUSTOMER

1. For correct polarity insert the batteries in the device correctly. If possible, design the battery holder so it will only hold the battery in the correct polarity. If this is not feasible, clearly mark or label the battery positions in the holder.
2. Make sure the customer knows the right type and size battery the product will use. Identify this on the label and in the operating instructions.
3. Suggest to the customer that all batteries be replaced at the same time.
4. Suggest that the customer check or clean the contact surface of the holder terminals when replacing the batteries.
5. Tell the customer to remove the batteries when the product is not in use for a prolonged period.
6. Caution the customer as to the dangers of attempting to recharge primary batteries and how to properly dispose of used batteries.
7. Tell the customer to check the condition of the batteries, either operationally or with a battery tester.
8. Tell the customer what the operational signs are that indicate the batteries should be replaced.

TESTING

The designer's or manufacturer's testing procedures should conform to the American National Standards Institute Bulletin C18.1, Dry Cells and Batteries.

STORAGE

Fresh batteries may be stored at room temperature 70°F (21°C) for moderate lengths of time with minor loss in capacity. Storage life may be extended by storing at lower temperatures but above freezing. Check the recommended storage temperature for the specific type of battery being stored.

ENERCELL BATTERY DATA AND SPECIFICATIONS

The following section is a collection of Enercell battery data and specifications currently available. The first page for every battery lists the basic specifications, designation, and physical profile with dimensions. Dimensions are given in inches and millimeters.

- Inches are in fractions to nearest equivalent or two decimal places. Decimal inches are nominal dimensions. Typical tolerances are normally in fractions.
- Millimeters are to one or two decimal places.

Service data for Enercell batteries follows. When comparing service data, note temperature, schedule, load, and time-to-cutoff voltage. Voltage discharge curves also are given for some Enercells.

Recommended discharge and charge rates also are listed for Enercell rechargeable batteries.

DATA AND SPECIFICATIONS CONTENTS

Note: See page 228 for a detailed index, which references the battery data by battery size, battery material type, and catalog number.

Type: **Carbon Zinc**
ANSI Designation: **"D"**
Suggested Current Range: **0-150 milliamperes**

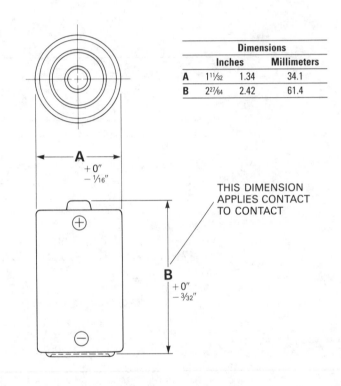

	Dimensions		
		Inches	Millimeters
A	1¹¹⁄₃₂	1.34	34.1
B	2²⁷⁄₆₄	2.42	61.4

A
+0"
− ¹⁄₁₆"

THIS DIMENSION
APPLIES CONTACT
TO CONTACT

B
+0"
− ³⁄₃₂"

Specifications

Voltage Taps	—, + 1.5
Terminals	Flat Contacts
Average Weight	3.07 oz. (93.3 grams)
Volume	3.19 cubic inches (52.3 cubic centimeters)
Jacket	Metal

Service data is on next page.

ENERCELL® General Purpose D Cell

Estimated Average Service at 70°F (21.1°C)

SCHEDULE	STARTING DRAINS (milliamperes)	LOAD (ohms)	CUTOFF VOLTAGE 0.8V	0.9V	1.0V
1 hour/day	385	3.9			7.5 hours
4 hours/day	37.5	40.0		155 hours	
Continous	667	2.25	135 minutes		

ENERCELL® Heavy Duty D Cell

Catalog No. **1.5**
23-580   VOLTS

Type: **Zinc Chloride**
ANSI Designation: **"D"**
Suggested Current Range: **0-150 milliamperes**

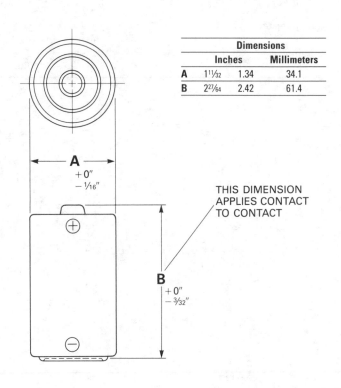

	Dimensions		
		Inches	Millimeters
A	1¹¹⁄₃₂	1.34	34.1
B	2²⁷⁄₆₄	2.42	61.4

A
+0"
−¹⁄₁₆"

THIS DIMENSION
APPLIES CONTACT
TO CONTACT

B
+0"
−³⁄₃₂"

Specifications

Voltage Taps	—, + 1.5
Terminals	Flat Contacts
Average Weight	3.74 oz. (106.1 grams)
Volume	3.19 cubic inches (52.3 cubic centimeters)
Jacket	Metal

Service data is on next page.

ENERCELL® Heavy Duty D Cell

Estimated Average Service at 70°F (21.1°C)

SCHEDULE	STARTING DRAINS (milliamperes)	LOAD (ohms)	CUTOFF VOLTAGE 0.8V	0.9V	1.0V
1 hour/day	385	3.9			18.5 hours
4 hours/day	37.5	40.0		240 hours	
Continuous	667	2.25	435 minutes		

Type: **Alkaline-Manganese Dioxide**
ANSI/NEDA Designation: **13A**
IEC Designation: **LR20**
Suggested Current Range: **0-650 milliamperes**

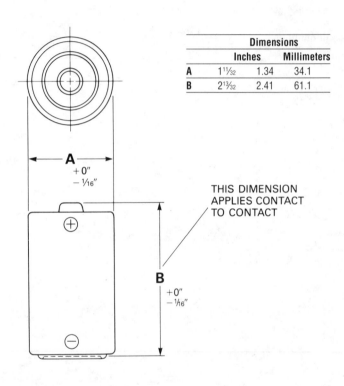

Dimensions		
	Inches	Millimeters
A	1¹¹⁄₃₂ 1.34	34.1
B	2¹³⁄₃₂ 2.41	61.1

A
+0″
−¹⁄₁₆″

THIS DIMENSION
APPLIES CONTACT
TO CONTACT

B
+0″
−¹⁄₁₆″

Specifications

Voltage Taps	−, + 1.5
Terminals	Flat Contacts
Average Weight	5.01 oz. (141.9 grams)
Volume	3.41 cubic inches (55.9 cubic centimeters)
Jacket	Insulated

Service data is on the next page.

Rev. 2/90

ENERCELL® Long Lasting D Cell

Estimated Average Hours Service at 70°F (21.1°C)

SCHEDULE	STARTING DRAINS (microamperes)	LOAD (ohms)	CUTOFF VOLTAGE			
			0.75V	0.9V	1.0V	1.2V
2 hours/day	8	150	2150	2000	1600	1250
8 hours/day	80	15	195	155	135	82
24 hours/day	800	1.5	13.8	9.5	7.4	1.6
4 hours/day (Radio Test)	50	24	373	299		
4 hours/day (Recorder Test)	120	10	150	119		
4 minutes/hour 8 hours/day 16 hours rest (Light-Industrial Flashlight Test)	545	2.2	20.7	18.7		
Continuous (Toy Test)	545	2.2	28	19		
	1200	1.0	9.6	6		

ENERCELL® Long Lasting D Cell

Internal Resistance

Measurement Schedule: Background load at 23 ohms; pulse load at 2.3 ohms; and pulse duration of 2.0 seconds.

INTERNAL RESISTANCE (APPROXIMATE) VS. TEMPERATURE

TEMPERATURE		INTERNAL RESISTANCE (ohms)
F	C	
70	21.1	0.2
32	0	0.4
−4	−20	0.7

Simulated Radio Test

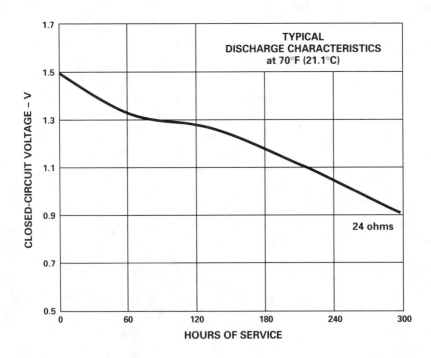

ENERCELL® Long Lasting D Cell

Estimated Average Hours Service at 70°F (21.1°C)

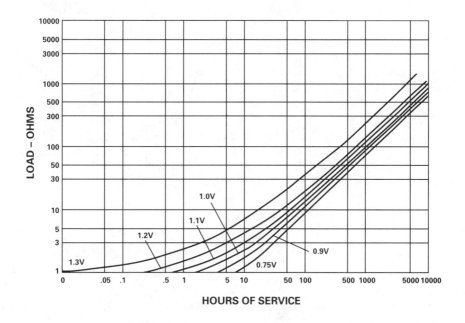

Type: **Nickel-Cadmium**
ANSI Designation: **"D"**
Suggested Current Range: **0-4.8 amperes**

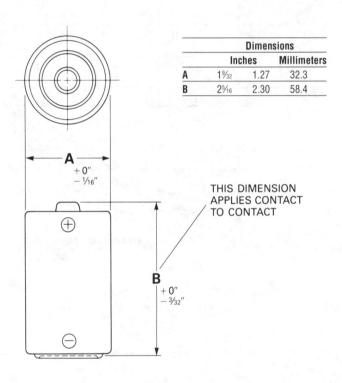

	Dimensions		
	Inches		Millimeters
A	1⁹⁄₃₂	1.27	32.3
B	2⁵⁄₁₆	2.30	58.4

A
+ 0″
− ¹⁄₁₆″

THIS DIMENSION
APPLIES CONTACT
TO CONTACT

B
+ 0″
− ³⁄₃₂″

Specifications

Voltage Taps	−, + 1.2
Terminals	Flat Contacts
Average Weight	2.30 oz. (65.1 grams)
Volume	3.2 cubic inches (52 cubic centimeters)
Jacket	Insulated

Service data is on the next page.

Rev. 2/90

ENERCELL® Rechargeable D Cell

Rated Capacity (AH)	
One hour rate (C rate)	1.400
Nominal C/5 (five hr. rate)	1.500
Maximum Continuous Discharge (A)	10
Charge Rate (mA) at 25°C	
16-20 hr. charge time	140
4-5 hr. charge time	475
Cell Temperature Limits (°C)	
Storage	−40 to +50°C
Cell under discharge	0 to +50°C
Cell under charge	0 to +50°C

CELL CHARACTERISTICS

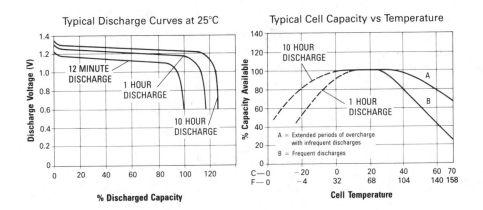

Typical Discharge Curves at 25°C

Typical Cell Capacity vs Temperature

Type: **Nickel-Cadmium**
ANSI Designation: **"D"**
Suggested Current Range: **0-10 amperes**

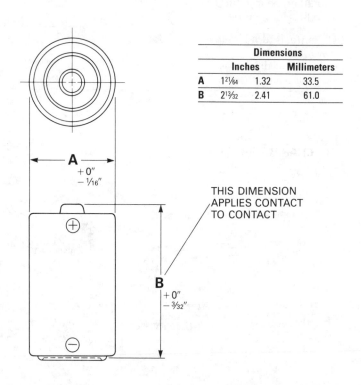

	Dimensions		
		Inches	Millimeters
A	$1^{21}/_{64}$	1.32	33.5
B	$2^{13}/_{32}$	2.41	61.0

A
+ 0"
− 1/16"

THIS DIMENSION
APPLIES CONTACT
TO CONTACT

B
+ 0"
− 3/32"

Specifications

Voltage Taps	—, + 1.2
Terminals	Flat Contacts
Average Weight	5.3 oz. (150 grams)
Volume	3.2 cubic inches (52 cubic centimeters)
Jacket	Insulated

Service data is on next page.

ENERCELL® Rechargeable Hi-Capacity D Cell

Rated Capacity (AH)	
One hour rate (C rate)	3.5
Nominal C/5 (five hr. rate)	4.0
C/10 (ten hr. rate)	4.3
High Rate Discharge (A)	4.0
Charge Rate (mA) at 25°C	
14-16 hr. charge time	400
Cell Temperature Limits (°C)	
Storage	−30 to +50°C
Cell under discharge	−20 to +60°C
Cell under charge	0 to +45°C

Type: **Carbon Zinc**
ANSI Designation: **"C"**
Suggested Current Range: **0-80 milliamperes**

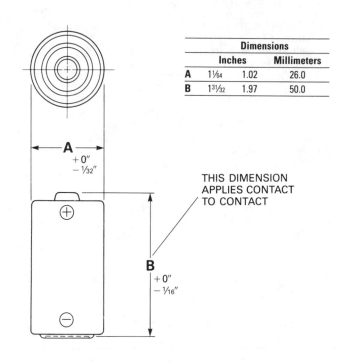

	Dimensions	
	Inches	**Millimeters**
A	1¹⁄₆₄ 1.02	26.0
B	1³¹⁄₃₂ 1.97	50.0

A
+ 0″
− ¹⁄₃₂″

THIS DIMENSION
APPLIES CONTACT
TO CONTACT

B
+ 0″
− ¹⁄₁₆″

Specifications

Voltage Taps	— , + 1.5
Terminals	Flat Contacts
Average Weight	1.59 oz. (45.1 grams)
Volume	1.5 cubic inches (24.8 cubic centimeters)
Jacket	Metal

Service data is on next page.

ENERCELL® General Purpose C Cell

Estimated Average Service at 70°F (21.1°C)

SCHEDULE	STARTING DRAINS (milliamperes)	LOAD (ohms)	CUTOFF VOLTAGE		
			0.8V	0.9V	1.0V
1 hour/day	221	6.8			5.0 hours
4 hours/day	20	75		125 hours	
Continuous	375	4	110 minutes		

Type: **Zinc Chloride**
ANSI Designation: **"C"**
Suggested Current Range: **0-80 milliamperes**

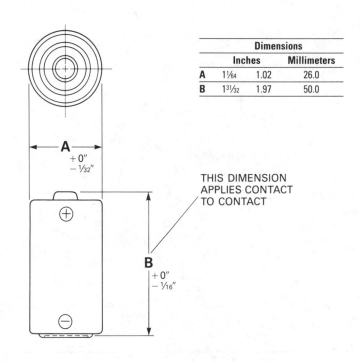

	Dimensions		
	Inches		Millimeters
A	1 1/64	1.02	26.0
B	1 31/32	1.97	50.0

THIS DIMENSION
APPLIES CONTACT
TO CONTACT

Specifications

Voltage Taps	—, + 1.5
Terminals	Flat Contacts
Average Weight	1.8 oz. (51.1 grams)
Volume	1.5 cubic inches (24.8 cubic centimeters)
Jacket	Metal

Service data is on next page.

ENERCELL® Heavy Duty C Cell

Estimated Average Service at 70°F (21.1°C)

SCHEDULE	STARTING DRAINS (milliamperes)	LOAD (ohms)	CUTOFF VOLTAGE 0.8V	0.9V	1.0V
1 hour/day	221	6.8			15 hours
4 hours/day	20	75		200 hours	
Continuous	375	4	390 minutes		

Type: **Alkaline-Manganese Dioxide**
ANSI/NEDA Designation: **L70**
IEC Designation: **LR14**
Suggested Current Range: **0-480 milliamperes**

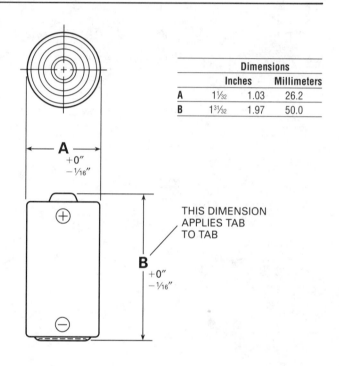

	Dimensions		
	Inches		Millimeters
A	1 1/32	1.03	26.2
B	1 31/32	1.97	50.0

A
+0″
−1/16″

THIS DIMENSION
APPLIES TAB
TO TAB

B
+0″
−1/16″

Specifications

Voltage Taps	−, + 1.5
Terminals	Flat Contacts
Average Weight	2.38 oz. (67.5 grams)
Volume	1.64 cubic inches (26.9 cubic centimeters)
Jacket	Insulated

Service data is on the next page.   *Rev. 2/90*

ENERCELL® Long Lasting C Cell

Estimated Average Hours Service at 70°F (21.1°C)

SCHEDULE	STARTING DRAINS (microamperes)	LOAD (ohms)	CUTOFF VOLTAGE			
			0.75V	0.9V	1.0V	1.2V
2 hours/day	8	150	1150	1050	950	720
8 hours/day	80	15	87	75	66	46
24 hours/day	800	1.5	5.6	4.1	2.5	0.58
4 hours/day (Radio Test)	16	75	509	483	378	
	31	39	268	226	189	
1 hour/day (Recorder Test)	120	10	60	50	45	
1 hour/day (Boom Box Test)	308	3.9	21.2	17.5	15.7	
1 hour/day (Compact Disk Test)	545	2.2	11.5	9.0	6.4	
4 minutes/hour 8 hours/day 16 hours rest (Light-Industrial Flashlight Test)	308	3.9	20.8	17.1	14.7	
Continuous (Toy Test)	308	3.9	20.4	16.2	15.0	

ENERCELL® Long Lasting C Cell

Internal Resistance

Measurement Schedule: Background load at 52 ohms; pulse load at 2.3 ohms; and pulse duration of 2.0 seconds.

INTERNAL RESISTANCE (APPROXIMATE) VS. TEMPERATURE

| TEMPERATURE | | INTERNAL RESISTANCE (ohms) |
F	C	
70	21.1	0.3
32	0	0.5
−4	−20	0.8

Simulated Radio Test

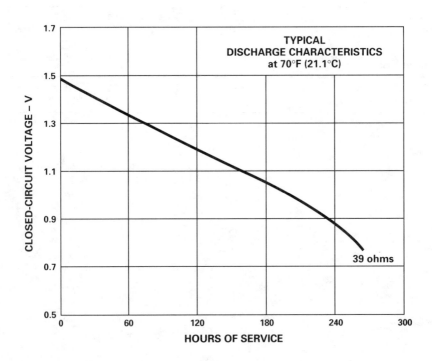

ENERCELL® Long Lasting C Cell

Estimated Average Hours Service at 70°F (21.1°C)

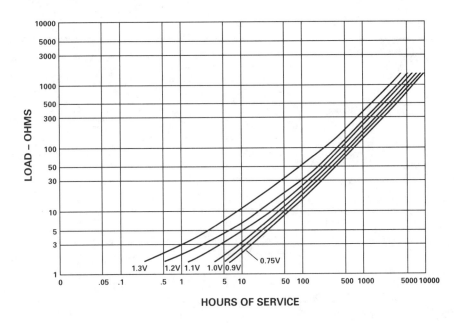

HOURS OF SERVICE

Type: **Nickel-Cadmium**
ANSI Designation: **"C"**
Suggested Current Range: **0-4.8 amperes**

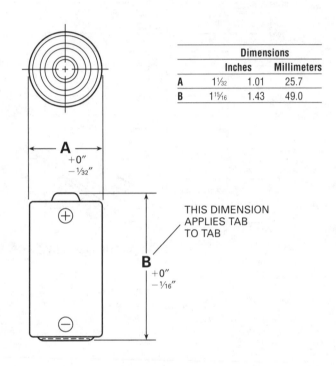

	Dimensions		
		Inches	Millimeters
A	1¹⁄₃₂	1.01	25.7
B	1¹⁵⁄₁₆	1.43	49.0

A
+0"
−¹⁄₃₂"

B
+0"
−¹⁄₁₆"

THIS DIMENSION
APPLIES TAB
TO TAB

Specifications

Voltage Taps	−, + 1.2
Terminals	Flat Contacts
Average Weight	1.8 oz. (50.9 grams)
Volume	1.53 cubic inches (25.1 cubic centimeters)
Jacket	Insulated

Service data is on the next page.

Rev. 2/90

ENERCELL® Rechargeable C Cell

Rated Capacity (AH)	
One hour rate (C rate)	1.400
Nominal C/5 (five hr. rate)	1.500
High Rate Discharge (A)	10
Charge Rate (mA) at 25°C	
16-20 hr. charge time	140
4-5 hr. charge time	475
Cell Temperature Limits (°C)	
Storage	−40 to +50°C
Cell under discharge	0 to +50°C
Cell under charge	0 to +50°C

CELL CHARACTERISTICS

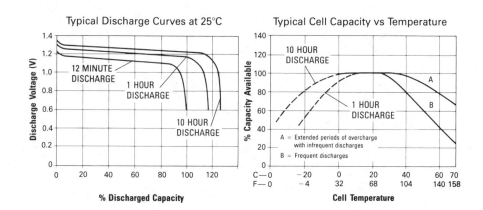

Typical Discharge Curves at 25°C

% Discharged Capacity

Typical Cell Capacity vs Temperature

A = Extended periods of overcharge with infrequent discharges

B = Frequent discharges

Cell Temperature

Type: **Nickel-Cadmium**
ANSI Designation: **"C"**
Suggested Current Range: **0-3.5 amperes**

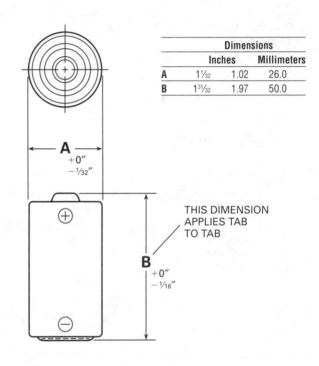

	Dimensions		
		Inches	Millimeters
A	1¹⁄₃₂	1.02	26.0
B	1³¹⁄₃₂	1.97	50.0

A
+0″
−¹⁄₃₂″

B
+0″
−¹⁄₁₆″

THIS DIMENSION
APPLIES TAB
TO TAB

Specifications

Voltage Taps	−, + 1.2
Terminals	Flat Contacts
Average Weight	2.5 oz. (70 grams)
Volume	1.53 cubic inches (25.1 cubic centimeters)
Jacket	Insulated

Service data is on the next page.

ENERCELL® Rechargeable Hi-Capacity C Cell

Rated Capacity (AH)	
One hour rate (C rate)	1.6
Nominal C/5 (five hr. rate)	1.8
C/10 (ten hr. rate)	2.0
High Rate Discharge (A)	1.8
Charge Rate (mA) at 25°C	
14-16 hr. charge time	180
Cell Temperature Limits (°C)	
Storage	−30 to +50°C
Cell under discharge	−20 to +60°C
Cell under charge	0 to +45°C

Type: **Nickel-Cadmium**
Designation: **"Sub C"**
Suggested Current Range: **0-4.8 amperes**

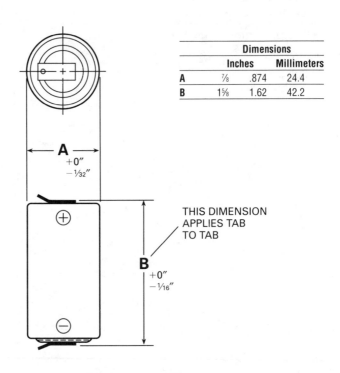

	Dimensions		
	Inches		Millimeters
A	⅞	.874	24.4
B	1⅝	1.62	42.2

A
+0″
−¹⁄₃₂″

B
+0″
−¹⁄₁₆″

THIS DIMENSION
APPLIES TAB
TO TAB

Specifications

Voltage Taps	−, + 1.2
Terminals	Solder Tabs
Average Weight	1.83 oz. (52.0 grams)
Volume	1.06 cubic inches (17.4 cubic centimeters)
Jacket	Insulated

Service data is on the next page.   *Rev. 2/90*

ENERCELL® Replacement Rechargeable Sub C Cell

Internal Resistance (at 50% discharge)	8mΩ
Rated Capacity (AH) One hour rate (C rate)	1.200
High Rate Discharge (A)	5

Charge Rate (mA) at 25°C
   Maximum (14-16 hr. charge time)
   Minimum
	120
	60

Cell Temperature Limits (°C)
   Storage
   Cell under discharge
   Cell under charge
	−40 to +50°C
	0 to +50°C
	0 to +50°C

CELL CHARACTERISTICS

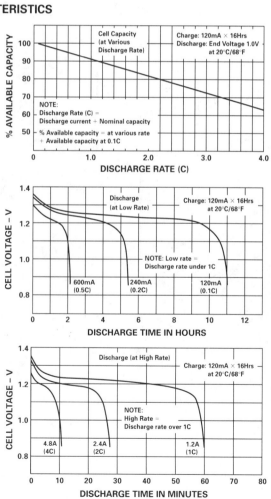

Type: **Lithium Manganese Dioxide**
Designation: **2/3A Size Component Cell**
Suggested Current Range: **See Discharge Data**

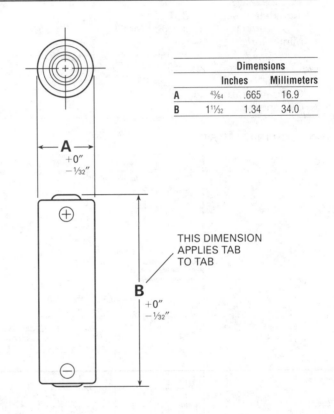

	Dimensions		
		Inches	Millimeters
A	43/64	.665	16.9
B	1 11/32	1.34	34.0

A
+0"
−1/32"

THIS DIMENSION
APPLIES TAB
TO TAB

B
+0"
−1/32"

Specifications

Voltage Taps	−, + 3.0
Terminals	Flat Contacts
Average Weight	0.56 oz. (16.0 grams)
Volume	0.422 cubic inch (6.9 cubic centimeters)
Jacket	Metal

Service data is on the next page.

ENERCELL® Lithium 2/3A Cell

Estimated Average Service at 70°F (21.1°C)

Continuous Duty

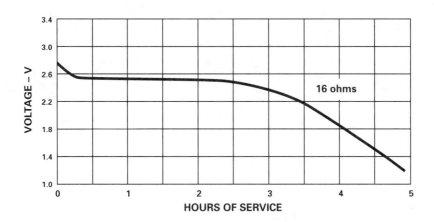

Pulsed Duty

Pulsed Service: 1.2 amperes load pulsed 3 seconds on and 7 seconds off.

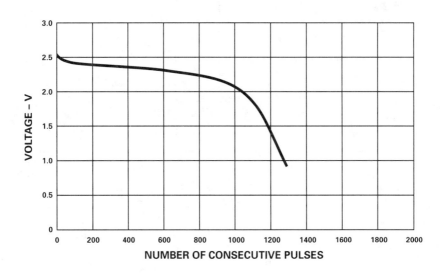

Type: **Carbon Zinc**
Designation: **"AA"**
Suggested Current Range: **0-25 milliamperes**

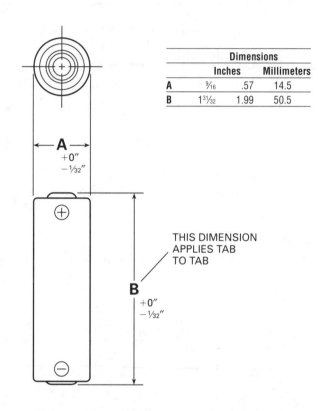

	Dimensions		
		Inches	Millimeters
A	$^9/_{16}$	.57	14.5
B	$1^{31}/_{32}$	1.99	50.5

THIS DIMENSION
APPLIES TAB
TO TAB

Specifications

Voltage Taps	−, + 1.5
Terminals	Flat Contacts
Average Weight	0.53 oz. (15.1 grams)
Volume	0.439 cubic inch (7.19 cubic centimeters)
Jacket	Metal

Service data is on the next page.

ENERCELL® General Purpose AA Cell

Estimated Average Service at 70°F (21.1°C)

SCHEDULE	STARTING DRAIN (millamperes)	LOAD (ohms)	CUTOFF VOLTAGE 0.8V	0.9V
1 hours/day	150	10		7.5 hours
4 hours/day	20	75		40 hours
Continuous	375	4	49 minutes	

ENERCELL® Heavy Duty AA Cell

Catalog No.
23-582

1.5
VOLTS

Type: **Zinc Chloride**
Designation: **"AA"**
Suggested Current Range: **0-25 milliamperes**

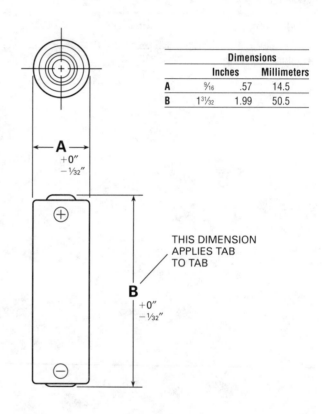

	Dimensions		
		Inches	Millimeters
A	$9/16$	.57	14.5
B	$1^{31}/_{32}$	1.99	50.5

THIS DIMENSION
APPLIES TAB
TO TAB

A
+0"
−1/32"

B
+0"
−1/32"

Specifications

Voltage Taps	−, + 1.5
Terminals	Flat Contacts
Average Weight	0.71 oz. (20.2 grams)
Volume	0.439 cubic inch (7.19 cubic centimeters)
Jacket	Metal

Service data is on the next page.

ENERCELL® Heavy Duty AA Cell

Estimated Average Service at 70°F (21.1°C)

SCHEDULE	STARTING DRAIN (millamperes)	LOAD (ohms)	CUTOFF VOLTAGE	
			0.8V	0.9V
1 hours/day	150	10		7.5 hours
4 hours/day	20	75		65 hours
Continuous	375	4	110 minutes	

Type: **Alkaline-Manganese Dioxide**
ANSI/NEDA Designation: **15A**
IEC Designation: **LR6**
Suggested Current Range: **0-250 milliamperes**

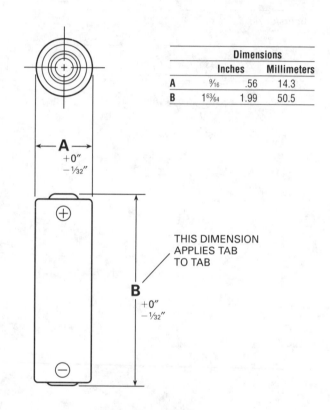

	Dimensions		
	Inches		Millimeters
A	$9/16$	.56	14.3
B	$1^{63}/_{64}$	1.99	50.5

THIS DIMENSION
APPLIES TAB
TO TAB

Specifications

Voltage Taps	−, + 1.5
Terminals	Flat Contacts
Average Weight	0.81 oz. (22.9 grams)
Volume	0.49 cubic inches (8.0 cubic centimeters)
Jacket	Insulated

Service data is on the next page.

Rev. 2/90

ENERCELL® Long Lasting AA Cell

Estimated Average Hours Service at 70°F (21.1°C)

SCHEDULE	STARTING DRAINS (microamperes)	LOAD (ohms)	CUTOFF VOLTAGE			
			0.75V	0.9V	1.0V	1.2V
2 hours/day	8	150	330	310	240	180
8 hours/day	80	15	33	28	24	14
24 hours/day	800	1.5	2	1.4	0.9	0.2
4 hours/day (Radio Test)	18	75	170	154	127	
1 hour/day (Calculator Test)	80	15	33	26	22	
1 hour/day (Cassette Test)	120	10	22	19	17	
1 hour/day (Compact Disk/TV Test)	308	3.9	7.7	6.0	4.8	
4 minutes/hour 8 hours/day 16 hours rest (Light-Industrial Flashlight Test)	308	3.9	7.1	5.8	5.0	
Continuous (Toy Test)	308	3.9	7.3	5.7	4.6	

ENERCELL® Long Lasting AA Cell

Internal Resistance

Measurement Schedule: Background load at 150 ohms; pulse load at 2.3 ohms; and pulse duration of 2.0 seconds.

INTERNAL RESISTANCE (APPROXIMATE) VS. TEMPERATURE

TEMPERATURE		INTERNAL RESISTANCE (ohms)
F	C	
70	21.1	0.2
32	0	0.4
−4	−20	0.8

Simulated Radio Test

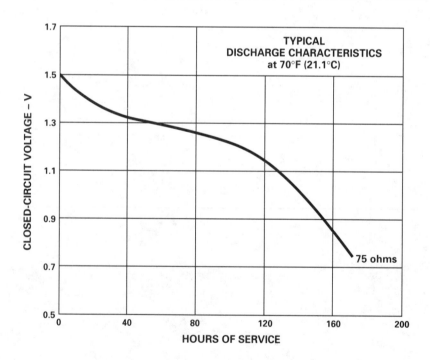

ENERCELL® Long Lasting AA Cell

Estimated Average Hours Service at 70°F (21.1°C)

TYPICAL CONTINUOUS PERFORMANCE CHARACTERISTICS

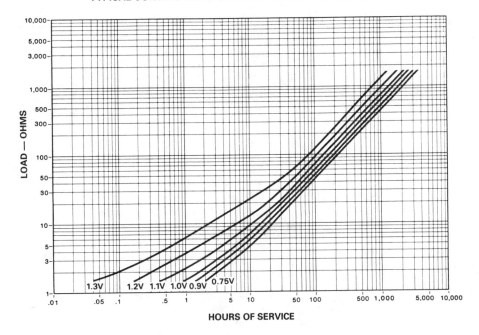

Type: **Nickel-Cadmium**
ANSI Designation: **"AA"**
Suggested Current Range: **0-2.0 amperes**

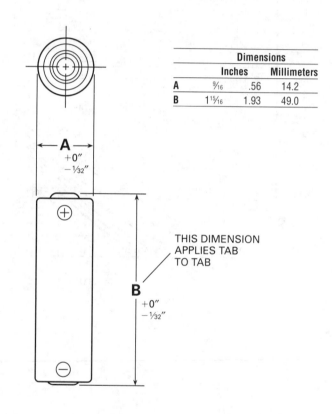

	Dimensions		
	Inches		Millimeters
A	9/16	.56	14.2
B	1 15/16	1.93	49.0

A
+0"
−1/32"

THIS DIMENSION
APPLIES TAB
TO TAB

B
+0"
−1/32"

Specifications

Voltage Taps	−, + 1.2
Terminals	Flat Contacts
Average Weight	0.85 oz. (24.0 grams)
Volume	0.48 cubic inches (7.86 cubic centimeters)
Jacket	Insulated

Service data is on the next page.

Rev. 2/90

ENERCELL® Rechargeable AA Cell

Rated Capacity (AH)	
One hour rate (C rate)	0.600
Nominal C/5 (five hr. rate)	0.650
Maximum Continuous Discharge (A)	5
Charge Rate (mA) at 25°C	
16-20 hr. charge time	60
5-6 hr. charge time	150
1 hour fast charge	700
Cell Temperature Limits (°C)	
Storage	−40 to +50°C
Cell under discharge	0 to +50°C
Cell under charge	0 to +50°C

CELL CHARACTERISTICS

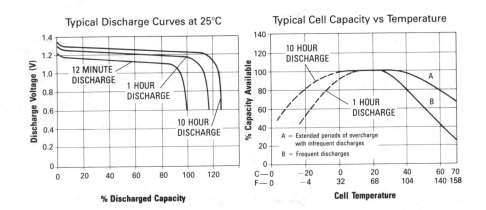

Typical Discharge Curves at 25°C

Typical Cell Capacity vs Temperature

Type: **Nickel-Cadmium**
ANSI Designation: **"AA"**
Suggested Current Range: **0-2.0 amperes**

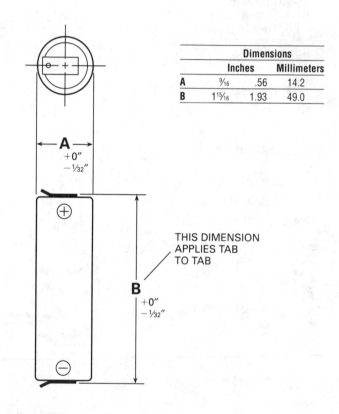

	Dimensions		
	Inches		Millimeters
A	⁹⁄₁₆	.56	14.2
B	1¹⁵⁄₁₆	1.93	49.0

THIS DIMENSION
APPLIES TAB
TO TAB

Specifications

Voltage Taps	−, + 1.2
Terminals	Solder Tabs
Average Weight	0.85 oz. (24.0 grams)
Volume	0.48 cubic inches (7.86 cubic centimeters)
Jacket	Insulated

Service data is on the next page.

ENERCELL® Replacement Rechargeable AA Cell

Rated Capacity (AH)	
One hour rate (C rate)	0.600
Nominal C/5 (five hr. rate)	0.650

Maximum Continuous Discharge (A)	5

Charge Rate (mA) at 25°C	
16-20 hr. charge time	60
5-6 hr. charge time	150
1 hour fast charge	700

Cell Temperature Limits (°C)	
Storage	−40 to +50°C
Cell under discharge	0 to +50°C
Cell under charge	0 to +50°C

CELL CHARACTERISTICS

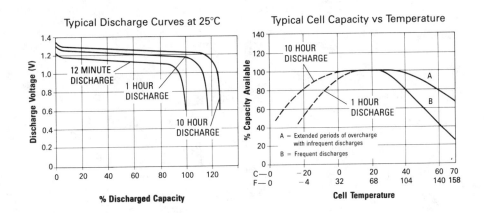

Typical Discharge Curves at 25°C

Typical Cell Capacity vs Temperature

Type: **Zinc Chloride**
ANSI Designation: **"AAA"**
Suggested Current Range: **0-20 milliamperes**

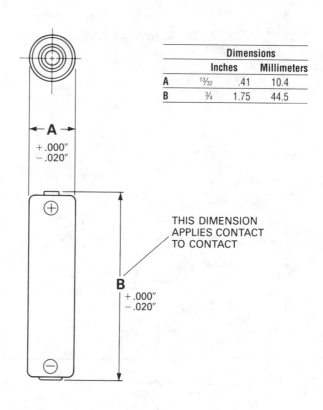

	Dimensions		
		Inches	Millimeters
A	¹³⁄₃₂	.41	10.4
B	¾	1.75	44.5

←**A**→
+ .000"
− .020"

B
+ .000"
− .020"

THIS DIMENSION
APPLIES CONTACT
TO CONTACT

Specifications

Voltage Taps	−, + 1.5
Terminals	Flat Contacts
Average Weight	0.32 oz. (9.1 grams)
Volume (by displacement)	0.201 cubic inch (3.29 cubic centimeters)
Jacket	Metal

Service data is on the next page.

ENERCELL® Heavy Duty AAA Cell

Estimated Average Service at 70°F (21.1°C)

SCHEDULE	STARTING DRAINS (milliamperes)	LOAD (ohms)	HOURS TO CUTOFF VOLTAGE 0.9V
5 minutes/day	300	5	1.5
12 hours/day	5	300	120

Type: **Alkaline-Manganese Dioxide**
ANSI/NEDA Designation: **24A**
IEC Designation: **LR03**
Suggested Current Range: **0-175 milliamperes**

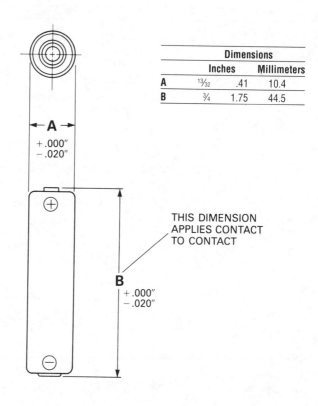

	Dimensions		
	Inches		Millimeters
A	13/32	.41	10.4
B	3/4	1.75	44.5

←**A**→
+.000″
−.020″

THIS DIMENSION
APPLIES CONTACT
TO CONTACT

B
+.000″
−.020″

Specifications

Voltage Taps	−, + 1.5
Terminals	Flat Contacts
Average Weight	0.41 oz. (11.6 grams)
Volume (by displacement)	0.23 cubic inches (3.8 cubic centimeters)
Jacket	Insulated

Service data is on the next page.   *Rev. 2/90*

ENERCELL® Long Lasting AAA Cell

Estimated Average Hours Service at 70°F (21.1°C)

SCHEDULE	STARTING DRAINS (microamperes)	LOAD (ohms)	CUTOFF VOLTAGE			
			0.75V	0.9V	1.0V	1.2V
2 hours/day	8	150	140	121	106	69
8 hours/day	80	15	12.5	9.8	8.2	2.6
24 hours/day	800	1.5	0.40	0.31	0.23	0.03
4 hours/day (Radio Test)	15	82	82	70	63	
1 hour/day (Calculator Test)	40	30	29	24	22	
5 minutes/day (General Purpose Intermittent Flashlight Test)	235	5.1	3.9	3.3	2.8	
4 minutes every 15 minutes 8 hours/day 16 hours rest (Camera Test)	250 constant current				2.4	

ENERCELL® Long Lasting AAA Cell

Internal Resistance

Measurement Schedule: Background load at 150 ohms; pulse load at 2.3 ohms; and pulse duration of 2.0 seconds.

INTERNAL RESISTANCE (APPROXIMATE) VS. TEMPERATURE

| TEMPERATURE | | INTERNAL RESISTANCE (ohms) |
F	C	
70	21.1	0.6
32	0	1.2
−4	−20	4.0

Simulated Radio Test

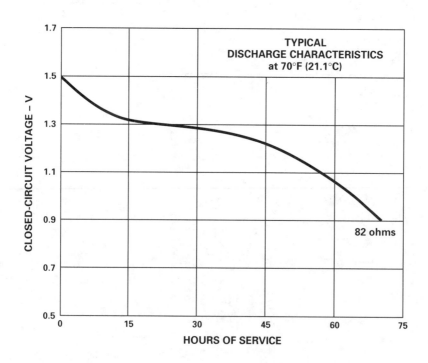

ENERCELL® Long Lasting AAA Cell

Estimated Average Hours Service at 70°F (21.1°C)

TYPICAL CONTINUOUS PERFORMANCE CHARACTERISTICS

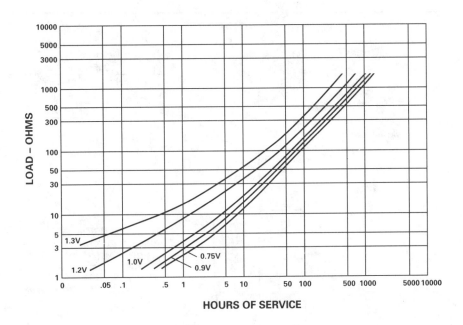

HOURS OF SERVICE

Type: **Nickel-Cadmium**
ANSI Designation: **"AAA"**
Suggested Current Range: **0-250 milliamperes**

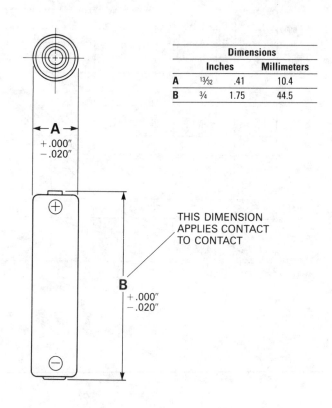

	Dimensions		
		Inches	Millimeters
A	¹³⁄₃₂	.41	10.4
B	¾	1.75	44.5

←**A**→
+.000"
−.020"

⊕

B
+.000"
−.020"

THIS DIMENSION
APPLIES CONTACT
TO CONTACT

⊖

Specifications

Voltage Taps	—, + 1.2
Terminals	Flat Contacts
Average Weight	0.37 oz. (10.5 grams)
Volume (by displacement)	0.201 cubic inch (3.29 cubic centimeters)
Jacket	Insulated

Service data is on next page.

ENERCELL® Rechargeable AAA Cell

Rated Capacity (AH)	
One hour rate (C rate)	0.150
Nominal C/5 (five hr. rate)	0.185
Maximum Continuous Discharge (A)	0.6
Charge Rate (mA) at 25°C	
Maximum (16-20 hr. charge time)	18
Minimum	9
Cell Temperature Limits (°C)	
Storage	-40 to $+50°C$
Cell under discharge	-20 to $+50°C$
Cell under charge	0 to $+50°C$

CELL CHARACTERISTICS

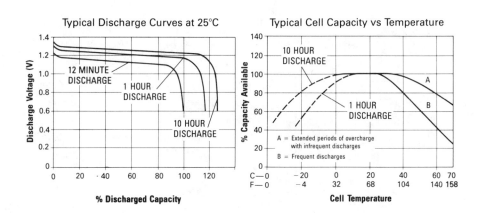

Typical Discharge Curves at 25°C

% Discharged Capacity

Typical Cell Capacity vs Temperature

A = Extended periods of overcharge with infrequent discharges

B = Frequent discharges

Cell Temperature

Type: **Zinc Chloride**
Suggested Current Range: **0-85 milliamperes**

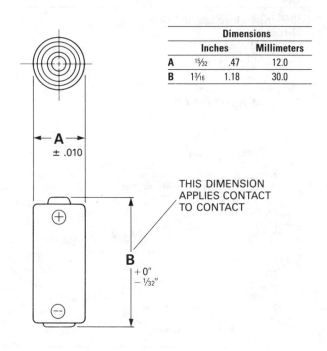

Dimensions		
	Inches	**Millimeters**
A	$^{15}/_{32}$ .47	12.0
B	$1^{3}/_{16}$ 1.18	30.0

A
± .010

THIS DIMENSION
APPLIES CONTACT
TO CONTACT

B
+ 0"
− ¹⁄₃₂"

Specifications

Voltage Taps	— , + 1.5
Terminals	Flat Contacts
Average Weight	0.23 oz. (6.5 grams)
Volume	0.17 cubic inch (2.8 cubic centimeters)
Jacket	Metal

Service data is on next page.

ENERCELL® Heavy Duty N Cell

Estimated Average Service at 70°F (21.1°C)

SCHEDULE	STARTING DRAINS (milliamperes)	LOAD (ohms)	HOURS TO CUTOFF VOLTAGE 0.9V
12 hours/day	5	300	85

Type: **Alkaline-Manganese Dioxide**
Suggested Current Range: **0-85 milliamperes**

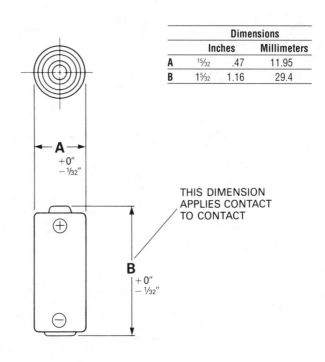

Dimensions		
	Inches	Millimeters
A	¹⁵⁄₃₂ .47	11.95
B	1⁵⁄₃₂ 1.16	29.4

A
+0″
− ¹⁄₃₂″

THIS DIMENSION
APPLIES CONTACT
TO CONTACT

B
+ 0″
− ¹⁄₃₂″

Specifications

Voltage Taps	−, + 1.5
Terminals	Flat Contacts
Average Weight	0.32 oz. (9.0 grams)
Volume	0.20 cubic inch (3.3 cubic centimeters)
Jacket	Insulated

Service data is on the next page.

Rev. 2/90

ENERCELL® Long Lasting N Cell

Estimated Average Hours Service at 70°F (21.1°C)

SCHEDULE	STARTING DRAIN (millamperes)	LOAD (ohms)	CUTOFF VOLTAGE	
			0.75V	0.9V
16 hours/day (Hearing Aid Test)	4	300	231	210
4 hours/day (Radio Test)	10	125	79	74
1 hour/day (Cassette Test)	40	30	20	17
5 minutes/hour (General Purpose Intermittent Test-Flashlight)	235	5.1	2.5	2.1

Simulated Radio Test

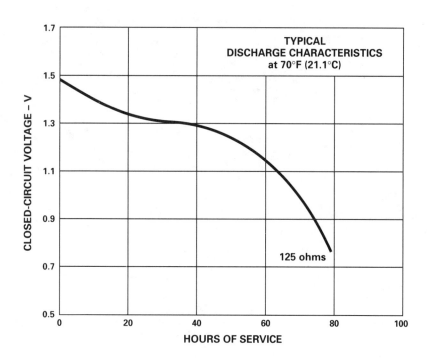

Type: **Nickel-Cadium**
Suggested Current Range: **0-250 milliamperes**

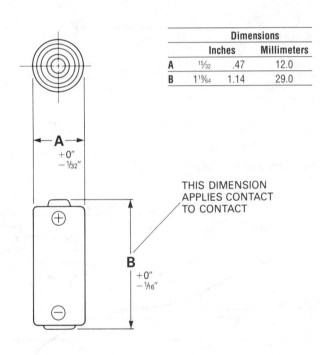

Dimensions		
	Inches	**Millimeters**
A	$^{15}/_{32}$ .47	12.0
B	$1^{19}/_{64}$ 1.14	29.0

A
+0″
− $^1/_{32}$″

THIS DIMENSION
APPLIES CONTACT
TO CONTACT

B
+0″
− $^1/_{16}$″

Specifications

Voltage Taps	−, + 1.5
Terminals	Flat Contacts
Average Weight	0.32 oz. (9.0 grams)
Volume	0.17 cubic inch (2.8 cubic centimeters)
Jacket	Insulated

Service data is on the next page.   *Rev. 2/90*

ENERCELL® Rechargeable N Cell

Rated Capacity (AH) One hour rate (C rate)	0.150
Maximum Continuous Discharge (A)	1.2
Charge Rate (mA) at 25°C Maximum (14-16 hr. charge time)	15
Cell Temperature Limits (°C) Storage Cell under discharge Cell under charge	−30 to +50°C −20 to +60°C 0 to +45°C

CELL CHARACTERISTICS

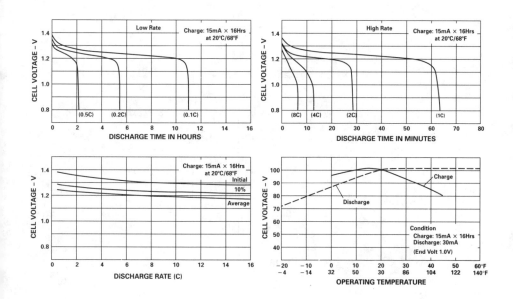

Type: **Carbon Zinc**
ANSI Designation: **4 Fd**
Suggested Current Range: **0-250 milliamperes**

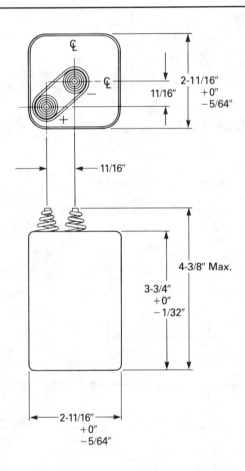

Specifications

Voltage Taps	—, + 6
Terminals	Spring
Average Weight	1 lb. - 6 oz. (623 grams)
Volume	31 cubic inches (508 cubic centimeters)
Jacket	Metal

Service data is on next page.

ENERCELL® General Purpose 6V Lantern

Estimated Average Service at 70°F (21.1°C)

SCHEDULE	STARTING DRAINS (milliamperes)	LOAD (ohms)	HOURS TO CUTOFF VOLTAGE		
			3.6V	3.0V	2.6V
30 min/hr 8 hrs/day	667	9	7.0	9.5	12.0
30 min/hr 8 hrs/day	188	32	42.0		

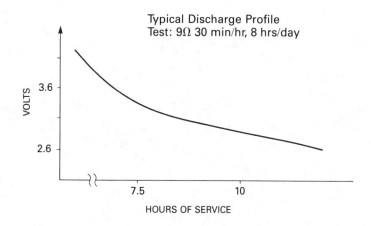

Typical Discharge Profile
Test: 9Ω 30 min/hr, 8 hrs/day

Type: **Zinc Chloride**
ANSI Designation: **4 Fd**
Suggested Current Range: **0-250 milliamperes**

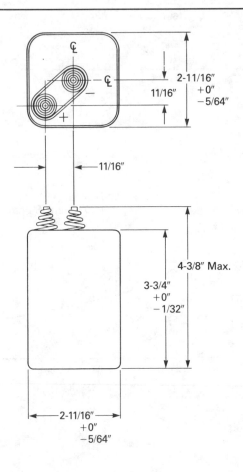

Specifications

Voltage Taps	—, + 6
Terminals	Spring
Average Weight	1 lb. - 6 oz. (623 grams)
Volume	31 cubic inches (508 cubic centimeters)
Jacket	Metal

Service data is on next page.

ENERCELL® Heavy Duty 6V Lantern

Estimated Average Service at 70°F (21.1°C)

SCHEDULE	STARTING DRAINS (milliamperes)	LOAD (ohms)	HOURS TO CUTOFF VOLTAGE		
			3.6V	3.0V	2.6V
30 min/hr 8 hrs/day	667	9	11.0	15.0	17.5
0.25 sec/sec 24 hrs/day	100	60	470		

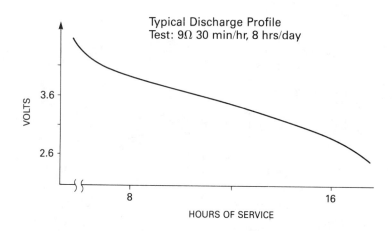

Typical Discharge Profile
Test: 9Ω 30 min/hr, 8 hrs/day

Type:　**Carbon Zinc**
Suggested Current Range: **0-15 milliamperes**

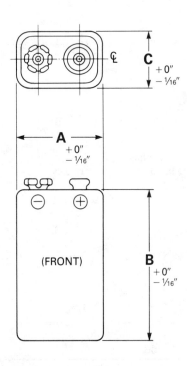

	Dimensions		
		Inches	Millimeters
A	1 1/32	1.03	26.2
B	1 15/16	1.94	49.2
C	11/16	.69	17.5

C
+0"
− 1/16"

A
+0"
− 1/16"

(FRONT)

B
+0"
− 1/16"

TERMINALS:
MINIATURE SNAP TYPE
ANSI NO. XVII

Specifications

Voltage Taps	—, + 9
Terminals	Miniature Snap
Average Weight	1.31 oz (37.1 grams)
Volume	1.28 cubic inches (21 cubic centimeters)
Jacket	Metal

Service data is on next page.

ENERCELL® General Purpose 9V Rect.

Estimated Average Service at 70°F (21.1°C)

SCHEDULE	STARTING DRAINS (milliamperes)	LOAD (ohms)	HOURS TO CUTOFF VOLTAGE 5.4V
4 hours/day	10	900	32
4 hours/day	15	600	18

Type: **Zinc Chloride**
Suggested Current Range: **0-15 milliamperes**

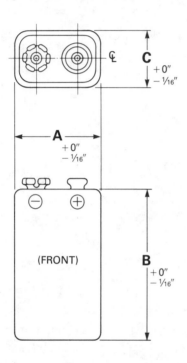

	Dimensions		
	Inches		**Millimeters**
A	1½2	1.02	26.0
B	1²⁹⁄32	1.93	49.0
C	1¹⁄16	.69	17.5

TERMINALS:
MINIATURE SNAP TYPE
ANSI NO. XVII

Specifications

Voltage Taps	—, + 9
Terminals	Miniature Snap
Average Weight	1.36 oz. (34.5 grams)
Volume	1.28 cubic inches (21 cubic centimeters)
Jacket	Metal

Service data is on next page.

ENERCELL® Heavy Duty 9V Rect.

Estimated Average Service at 70°F (21.1°C)

SCHEDULE	STARTING DRAINS (milliamperes)	LOAD (ohms)	HOURS TO CUTOFF VOLTAGE 5.4V
1 hour/day	50	180	6.5
4 hours/day	10	900	49
Continuous	40	225	6.5

Type: **Alkaline-Manganese Dioxide**
ANSI/NEDA Designation: **1604A**
IEC Designation: **6LR61**
Suggested Current Range: **0-100 milliamperes**

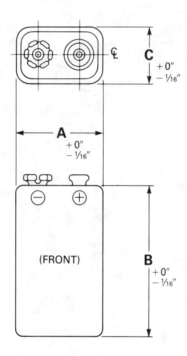

	Dimensions		
		Inches	Millimeters
A	1 1/32	1.03	26.2
B	1 15/16	1.94	49.2
C	11/16	.69	17.5

(FRONT)

TERMINALS:
MINATURE SNAP TYPE
ANSI NO. XVII

Specifications

Voltage Taps	−, + 9
Terminals	Miniature Snaps
Average Weight	1.65 oz. (46.7 grams)
Volume	1.28 cubic inches (21 cubic centimeters)
Jacket	Metal

Service data is on the next page.

Rev. 2/90

ENERCELL® Long Lasting 9V Rect.

Estimated Average Hours Service at 70°F (21.1°C)

SCHEDULE	STARTING DRAIN (millamperes)	LOAD (ohms)	HOURS TO CUTOFF VOLTAGE	
			4.2V	5.4V
4 hours/day (Radio Test)	14	510	43	37
½ hours/day (Calulator Test)	40	180	14	12
1 hour/day (Recorder Test)	40	180	15	13
1 hour/day (Toy Test)	27	270	21	19

Simulated Radio Test

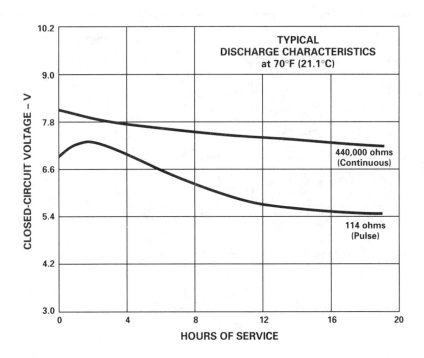

Measurement Schedule: Background load is 440,000 ohms; pulse load is 114 ohms and pulse duration is 2.0 seconds. Test is conducted once per week.

ENERCELL® Long Lasting 9V Rect.

Internal Resistance

Measurement Schedule: Background load at 3,600 ohms; pulse load at 13.8 ohms and pulse duration of 2.0 seconds.

INTERNAL RESISTANCE (APPROXIATE) VS. TEMPERATURE

| TEMPERATURE | | INTERNAL RESISTANCE (ohms) |
F	C	
70	21.1	2.0
32	0	4.0
−4	−20	8.0

Simulated Radio Test

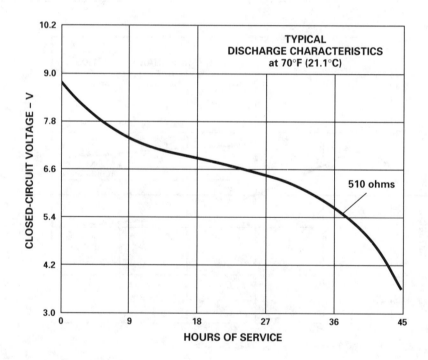

TYPICAL
DISCHARGE CHARACTERISTICS
at 70°F (21.1°C)

510 ohms

ENERCELL® Long Lasting 9V Rect.

Estimated Average Hours Service at 70°F (21.1°C)

TYPICAL CONTINUOUS PERFORMANCE CHARACTERISTICS

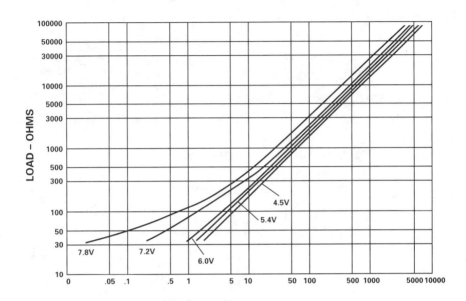

Type: **Nickel-Cadmium**
Suggested Current Range: **0-1 amperes**

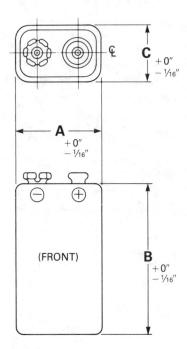

Dimensions			
	Inches		**Millimeters**
A	1 1/32	1.03	26.2
B	1 15/16	1.94	49.2
C	11/16	.66	16.8

(FRONT)

TERMINALS:
MINATURE SNAP TYPE
ANSI NO. XVII

Specifications

Voltage Taps	—, + 7.2
Terminals	Miniature Snap
Average Weight	1.25 oz. (35.7 grams)
Volume	1.28 cubic inches (21 cubic centimeters)
Jacket	Insulated

*For 9 volt applications

Service data is on next page.

ENERCELL® Rechargeable 9V Rect.

Rated Capacity (AH)	
One hour rate (C rate)	0.065
Nominal C/5 (five hr. rate)	0.080
Maximum Continuous Discharge (A)	1.0
Charge Rate (mA) at 25°C	
Maximum (16-20 hr. charge time)	7
Minimum	3
Cell Temperature Limits (°C)	
Storage	−40 to +50°C
Cell under discharge	−20 to +50°C
Cell under charge	0 to +50°C

CELL CHARACTERISTICS

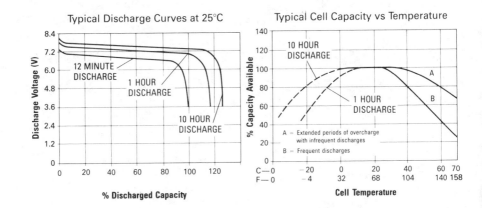

Typical Discharge Curves at 25°C

Typical Cell Capacity vs Temperature

Type: **Alkaline-Manganese Dioxide**
IEC Designation: **LR44**
THIS BATTERY IS DESIGNED FOR GENERAL ELECTRONIC
APPLICATIONS WHICH MAY REQUIRE HIGH RATE PULSES.

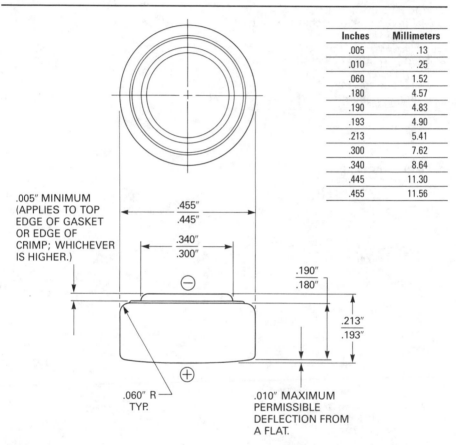

Inches	Millimeters
.005	.13
.010	.25
.060	1.52
.180	4.57
.190	4.83
.193	4.90
.213	5.41
.300	7.62
.340	8.64
.445	11.30
.455	11.56

.005″ MINIMUM
(APPLIES TO TOP
EDGE OF GASKET
OR EDGE OF
CRIMP; WHICHEVER
IS HIGHER.)

.455″
.445″

.340″
.300″

.190″
.180″

.213″
.193″

.060″ R
TYP.

.010″ MAXIMUM
PERMISSIBLE
DEFLECTION FROM
A FLAT.

Specifications

Voltage Taps	—, + 1.5
Average Service Capacity (to 0.9 volt) (Rated capacity at 15,000 ohm load at 21.1° C)	120 milliampere-hours
Terminals	Flat Contacts
Average Weight	0.08 oz. (2.3 grams)
Volume	0.03 cubic inch (0.5 cubic centimeter)

Service data is on next page.

ENERCELL® Type 357A

Estimated Average Service at 70°F (21.1°C)

SCHEDULE	STARTING DRAIN (microamperes)	LOAD (ohms)	CUTOFF VOLTAGE 0.9V
24 hours/day	100	15,000	1,375 hours

TYPICAL DISCHARGE CHARACTERISTICS
Voltage Discharge Curve at 70°F (21.1°C)

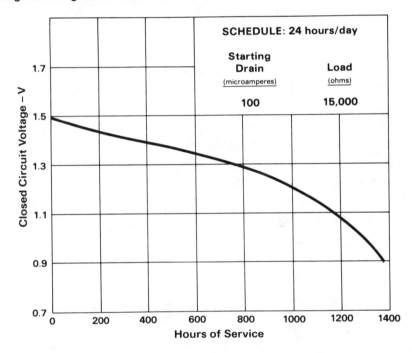

Bulge Data

This cell is bulge compensated so that it will not exceed a maximum height of 0.213" during discharge.

Internal Resistance

Closed circuit voltage no less than	1.2 volts
On a load of for 0.1 to 2 seconds	100 ohms

Type: **Alkaline-Manganese Dioxide**
IEC Designation: **LR43**
THIS BATTERY IS DESIGNED FOR GENERAL ELECTRONIC
APPLICATIONS WHICH MAY REQUIRE HIGH RATE PULSES.

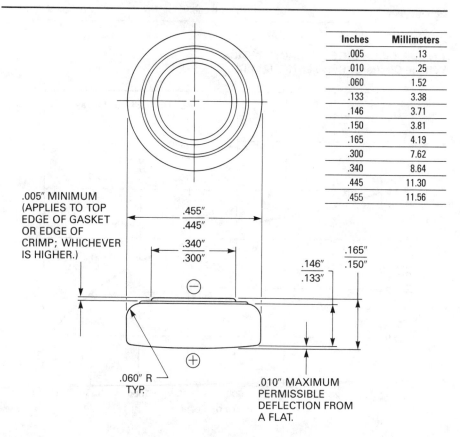

Inches	Millimeters
.005	.13
.010	.25
.060	1.52
.133	3.38
.146	3.71
.150	3.81
.165	4.19
.300	7.62
.340	8.64
.445	11.30
.455	11.56

.005" MINIMUM
(APPLIES TO TOP
EDGE OF GASKET
OR EDGE OF
CRIMP; WHICHEVER
IS HIGHER.)

.455"
.445"

.340"
.300"

.165"
.150"

.146"
.133"

.060" R
TYP.

.010" MAXIMUM
PERMISSIBLE
DEFLECTION FROM
A FLAT.

Specifications

Voltage Taps	—, + 1.5
Average Service Capacity (to 0.9 volt) (Rated capacity at 15,000 ohm load at 21.1° C)	90 milliampere-hours
Terminals	Flat Contacts
Average Weight	0.05 oz. (1.4 grams)
Volume	0.02 cubic inch (0.3 cubic centimeter)

Service data is on next page.

ENERCELL® Type 386A

Estimated Average Hours Service at 70°F (21.1°C)

SCHEDULE	STARTING DRAIN (microamperes)	LOAD (ohms)	CUTOFF VOLTAGE 0.9V
24 hours/day	100	15,000	1,100 hours

TYPICAL DISCHARGE CHARACTERISTICS
Voltage Discharge Curve at 70°F (21.1°C)

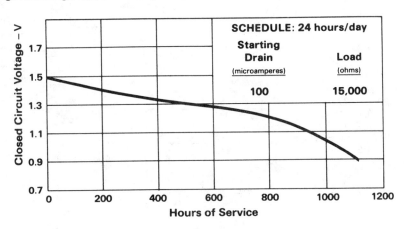

Bulge Data

This cell is bulge compensated so that it will not exceed a maximum height of 0.172" during discharge.

Internal Resistance

Closed circuit voltage no less than	1.2 volts
On a load of	100 ohms
for 0.1 to 2 seconds	

Type: **Alkaline-Manganese Dioxide**
IEC Designation: **LR54**
THIS BATTERY IS DESIGNED FOR GENERAL ELECTRONIC
APPLICATIONS WHICH MAY REQUIRE HIGH RATE PULSES.

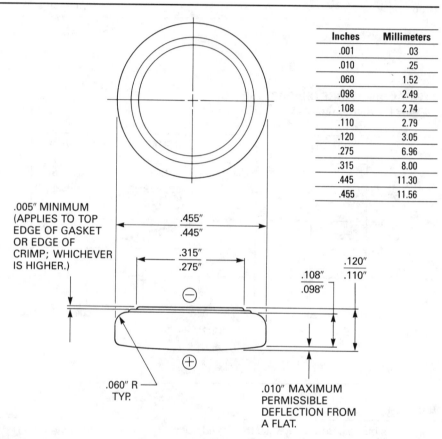

Inches	Millimeters
.001	.03
.010	.25
.060	1.52
.098	2.49
.108	2.74
.110	2.79
.120	3.05
.275	6.96
.315	8.00
.445	11.30
.455	11.56

.005″ MINIMUM
(APPLIES TO TOP
EDGE OF GASKET
OR EDGE OF
CRIMP; WHICHEVER
IS HIGHER.)

.455″
.445″

.315″
.275″

.120″
.110″

.108″
.098″

.060″ R
TYP.

.010″ MAXIMUM
PERMISSIBLE
DEFLECTION FROM
A FLAT.

Specifications

Voltage Taps	− , + 1.5
Average Service Capacity (to 0.9 volt) (Rated capacity at 15,000 ohm load at 21.1° C)	65 milliampere-hours
Terminals	Flat Contacts
Average Weight	0.04 oz. (1.1 grams)
Volume	0.02 cubic inch (0.3 cubic centimeter)

Service data is on next page.

ENERCELL® Type 389A

Estimated Average Hours Service at 70°F (21.1°C)

SCHEDULE	STARTING DRAIN (microamperes)	LOAD (ohms)	CUTOFF VOLTAGE 0.9V
24 hours/day	100	15,000	800 hours

TYPICAL DISCHARGE CHARACTERISTICS
Voltage Discharge Curve at 70°F (21.1°C)

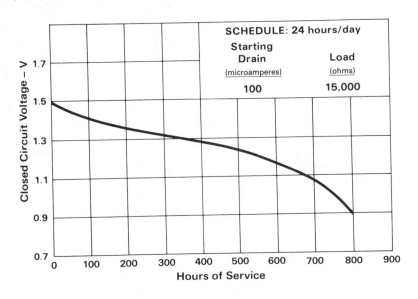

Bulge Data

This cell is bulge compensated so that it will not exceed a maximum height of 0.123" during discharge.

Internal Resistance

Closed circuit voltage no less than	1.2 volts
On a load of for 0.1 to 2 seconds	100 ohms

Type: **Alkaline-Manganese Dioxide**
IEC Designation: **LR55**
THIS BATTERY IS DESIGNED FOR GENERAL ELECTRONIC
APPLICATIONS WHICH MAY REQUIRE HIGH RATE PULSES.

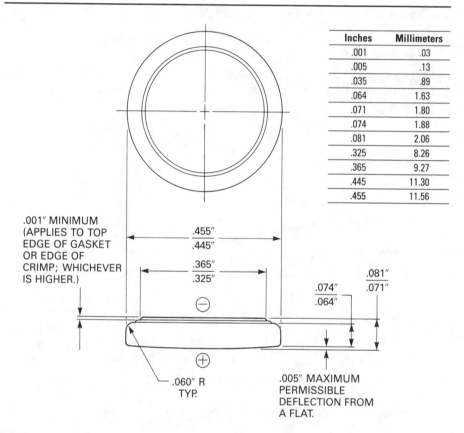

Inches	Millimeters
.001	.03
.005	.13
.035	.89
.064	1.63
.071	1.80
.074	1.88
.081	2.06
.325	8.26
.365	9.27
.445	11.30
.455	11.56

.001" MINIMUM
(APPLIES TO TOP
EDGE OF GASKET
OR EDGE OF
CRIMP; WHICHEVER
IS HIGHER.)

.455"
.445"

.365"
.325"

.081"
.071"

.074"
.064"

.060" R
TYP.

.005" MAXIMUM
PERMISSIBLE
DEFLECTION FROM
A FLAT.

Specifications

Voltage Taps	− , + 1.5
Average Service Capacity (to 0.9 volt) (Rated capacity at 15,000 ohm load at 21.1° C)	30 milliampere-hours
Terminals	Flat Contacts
Average Weight	0.03 oz. (0.9 gram)
Volume	0.01 cubic inch (0.2 cubic centimeters)

Service data is on next page.

ENERCELL® Type 391A

Estimated Average Hours Service at 70°F (21.1°C)

SCHEDULE	STARTING DRAIN (microamperes)	LOAD (ohms)	CUTOFF VOLTAGE 0.9V
24 hours/day	100	15,000	355 hours

TYPICAL DISCHARGE CHARACTERISTICS
Voltage Discharge Curve at 70°F (21.1°C)

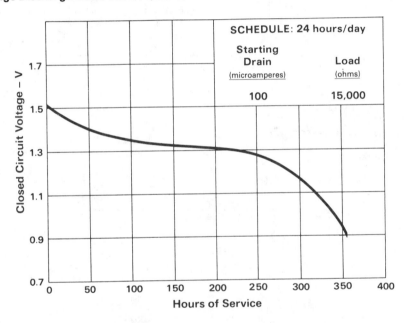

Bulge Data

This cell is bulge compensated so that it will not exceed a maximum height of 0.090" during discharge.

Internal Resistance

Closed circuit voltage no less than	1.2 volts
On a load of for 0.1 to 2 seconds	100 ohms

Type: **Silver Oxide**
ANSI Designation: **S15**
IEC Designation: **SR44**
DESIGNED SPECIFICALLY FOR PHOTO USE.

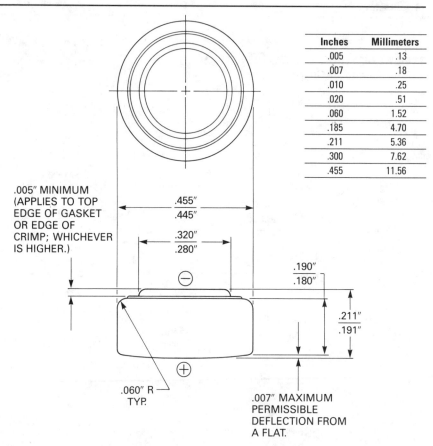

Inches	Millimeters
.005	.13
.007	.18
.010	.25
.020	.51
.060	1.52
.185	4.70
.211	5.36
.300	7.62
.455	11.56

.005" MINIMUM (APPLIES TO TOP EDGE OF GASKET OR EDGE OF CRIMP; WHICHEVER IS HIGHER.)

.455" / .445"

.320" / .280"

.190" / .180"

.211" / .191"

.060" R TYP.

.007" MAXIMUM PERMISSIBLE DEFLECTION FROM A FLAT.

Specifications

Voltage Taps	—, + 1.5
Average Service Capacity (to 1.3 volts) (Rated capacity at 6,500 ohm load at 35°C)	190 milliampere-hours
Terminals	Flat Contacts
Average Weight	0.080 oz. (2.27 grams)
Volume	0.029 cubic inch (0.48 cubic centimeter)

Service data is on next page.

ENERCELL® Type 76

Estimated Average Service at 95°F (35°C)

SCHEDULE	STARTING DRAIN (microamperes)	LOAD (ohms)	CUTOFF VOLTAGE	
			0.9V	1.3V
24 hours/day	242	6,500	820 hours	810 hours

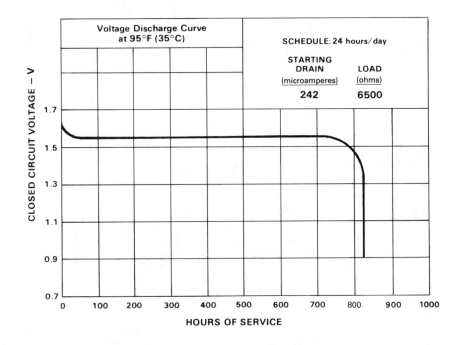

Internal Resistance

Closed circuit voltage no less than	1.2 volts
On a load of for 0.1 to 2 seconds	100 ohms

Type: **Silver Oxide**
IEC Designation: **SR54**
THIS BATTERY IS DESIGNED FOR USE ON CONTINUOUS
LOW DRAIN HIGH PULSE DRAIN ON DEMAND.

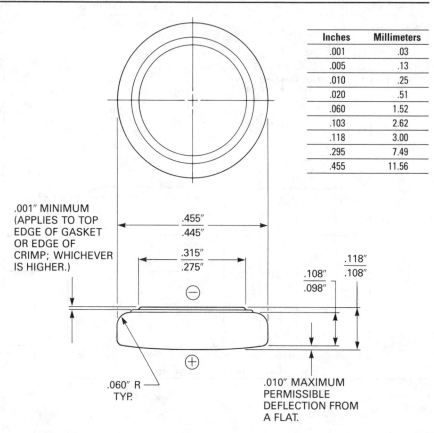

Inches	Millimeters
.001	.03
.005	.13
.010	.25
.020	.51
.060	1.52
.103	2.62
.118	3.00
.295	7.49
.455	11.56

.001" MINIMUM
(APPLIES TO TOP
EDGE OF GASKET
OR EDGE OF
CRIMP; WHICHEVER
IS HIGHER.)

.455"
.445"

.315"
.275"

.118"
.108"

.108"
.098"

.060" R
TYP.

.010" MAXIMUM
PERMISSIBLE
DEFLECTION FROM
A FLAT.

Specifications

Voltage Taps	—, + 1.5
Average Service Capacity (to 1.3 volts) (Rated capacity at 15,000 ohm load at 35°C)	85 milliampere-hours
Terminals	Flat Contacts
Average Weight	0.048 oz. (1.35 grams)
Volume	0.018 cubic inch (0.03 cubic centimeter)

Service data is on next page.

ENERCELL® Type 389

Estimated Average Service at 95°F (35°C)

SCHEDULE	STARTING DRAIN (microamperes)	LOAD (ohms)	CUTOFF VOLTAGE 1.3V
24 hours/day	105	15,000	825 hours
	10.6	150,000	335 days

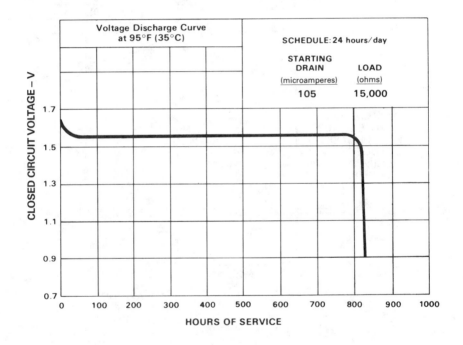

Voltage Discharge Curve at 95°F (35°C)

SCHEDULE: 24 hours/day

STARTING DRAIN (microamperes)	LOAD (ohms)
105	15,000

CLOSED CIRCUIT VOLTAGE – V

HOURS OF SERVICE

Internal Resistance

Closed circuit voltage no less than	1.2 volts
On a load of for 0.1 to 2 seconds	100 ohms

Type: **Silver Oxide**
IEC Designation: **SR41**
Suggested Current Range: **0-5 milliamperes**

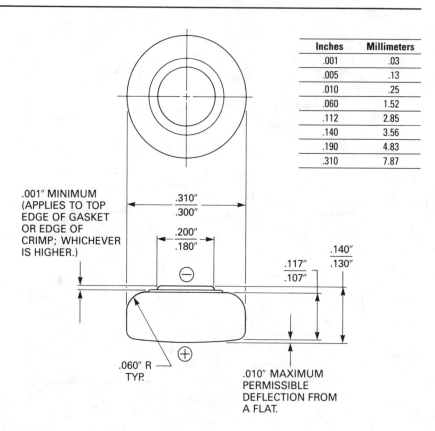

Inches	Millimeters
.001	.03
.005	.13
.010	.25
.060	1.52
.112	2.85
.140	3.56
.190	4.83
.310	7.87

.001" MINIMUM
(APPLIES TO TOP
EDGE OF GASKET
OR EDGE OF
CRIMP; WHICHEVER
IS HIGHER.)

.310"
.300"

.200"
.180"

.140"
.130"

.117"
.107"

⊖

.060" R
TYP.

⊕

.010" MAXIMUM
PERMISSIBLE
DEFLECTION FROM
A FLAT.

Specifications

Voltage Taps	—, + 1.5
Average Service Capacity (to 0.9 volt) (Rated capacity at 15,000 ohm load)	38 milliampere-hours
Terminals	Flat Contacts
Average Weight	0.02 oz. (0.57 gram)
Volume (by displacement)	0.01 cubic inch (0.16 cubic centimeter)

Service data is on next page.

ENERCELL® Type 392

Preliminary Performance Data at 95°F (35°C)

Background: 94000 ohms continuous (IC simulated load 16.8 microamperes)
Pulse Width: 2 seconds
Pulse Frequency: 100 ohms @ 12/day (LCD backlight simulation)

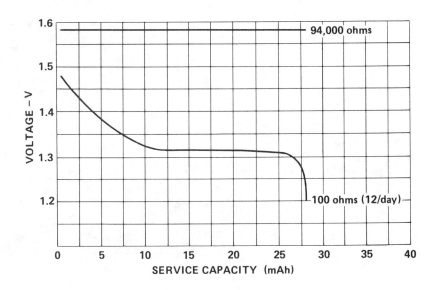

TYPICAL PULSE

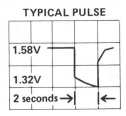

Estimated Service at 95°F (35°C)

SCHEDULE	STARTING DRAIN (microamperes)	LOAD (ohms)	CUTOFF VOLTAGE 1.3V
24 hours/day	104	15,000	370 hours

Type: **Silver Oxide**
ANSI Designation: **WS5**
Suggested Current Range: **0-5 milliamperes**

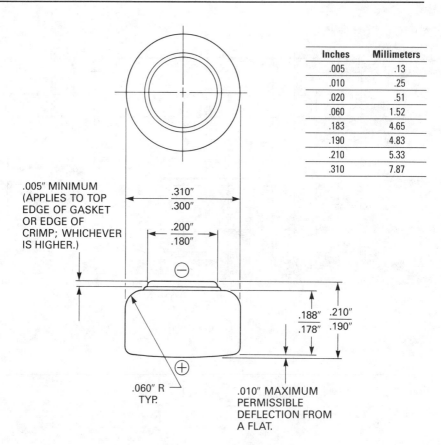

Inches	Millimeters
.005	.13
.010	.25
.020	.51
.060	1.52
.183	4.65
.190	4.83
.210	5.33
.310	7.87

.005″ MINIMUM
(APPLIES TO TOP
EDGE OF GASKET
OR EDGE OF
CRIMP; WHICHEVER
IS HIGHER.)

.310″
.300″

.200″
.180″

.188″ .210″
.178″ .190″

.060″ R
TYP.

.010″ MAXIMUM
PERMISSIBLE
DEFLECTION FROM
A FLAT.

Specifications

Voltage Taps	—, + 1.5
Average Service Capacity (to 0.9 volt) (Rated capacity at 15,000 ohm load)	75 milliampere-hours
Terminals	Flat Contacts
Average Weight	0.04 oz. (1.13 grams)
Volume (by displacement)	0.011 cubic inch (0.18 cubic centimeter)

Service data is on next page.

ENERCELL® Type 393

Preliminary Performance Data at 95°F (35°C)

Background: 94000 ohms continuous (IC simulated load 16.8 microamperes)
Pulse Width: 2 seconds
Pulse Frequency: 100 ohms @ 12/day (LCD backlight simulation)

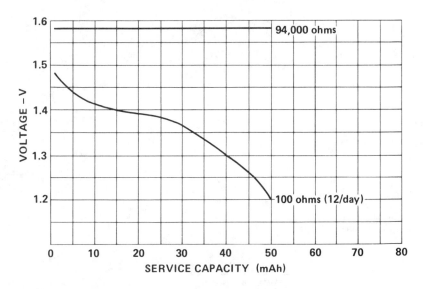

TYPICAL PULSE

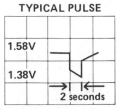

Estimated Service at 95°F (35°C)

SCHEDULE	STARTING DRAIN (microamperes)	LOAD (ohms)	CUTOFF VOLTAGE 1.3V
24 hours/day	104	15,000	725 hours

Type: **Silver Oxide**
ANSI Designation: **WS16**
IEC Designation: **SR47**
Suggested Current Range: **0-240 microamperes**

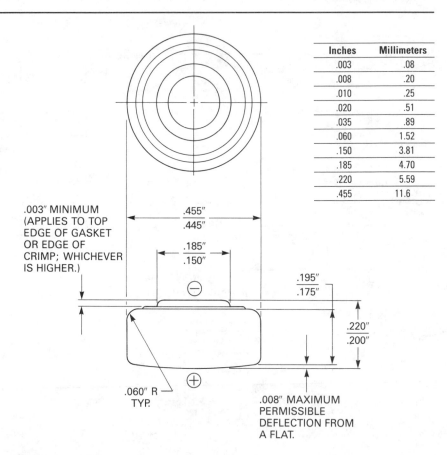

Inches	Millimeters
.003	.08
.008	.20
.010	.25
.020	.51
.035	.89
.060	1.52
.150	3.81
.185	4.70
.220	5.59
.455	11.6

.003″ MINIMUM
(APPLIES TO TOP
EDGE OF GASKET
OR EDGE OF
CRIMP; WHICHEVER
IS HIGHER.)

.455″
.445″

.185″
.150″

.195″
.175″

.220″
.200″

.060″ R
TYP.

.008″ MAXIMUM
PERMISSIBLE
DEFLECTION FROM
A FLAT.

Specifications

Voltage Taps	– , + 1.5
Average Service Capacity (to 1.3 volts) (Rated capacity at 6,500 ohm load)	165 milliampere-hours
Terminals	Flat Contacts
Average Weight	0.09 oz. (2.55 grams)
Volume (by displacement)	0.031 cubic inch (0.51 cubic centimeter)

Service data is on next page.

ENERCELL® Type 303

Estimated Average Service at 95°F (35°C)

SCHEDULE	STARTING DRAIN (microamperes)	LOAD (ohms)	CUTOFF VOLTAGE	
			0.9V	1.3V
24 hours/day	17	94,000	13 months	12.8 months
	246	6,500	700 hours	685 hours

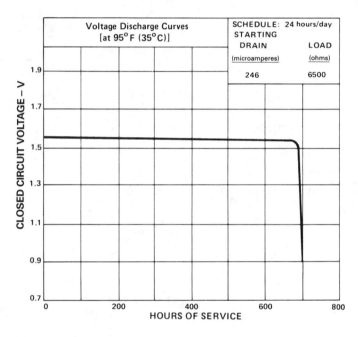

Service vs. Temperature

For following conditions:

Starting Drain:	205 microamperes
Load:	7800 ohms
Discharge Schedule:	24 hours/day
Cutoff:	1.3 volts

Temperature	% of 95°F Service vs. Temperature
113°F	94%
95°F	100%
70°F	95%
32°F	60%

Impedance

Approximate open circuit impedance at 1000 Hz: 27 ohms average

Type: **Silver Oxide**
IEC Designation: **SR44**
Suggested Current Range: **0-10 milliamperes**

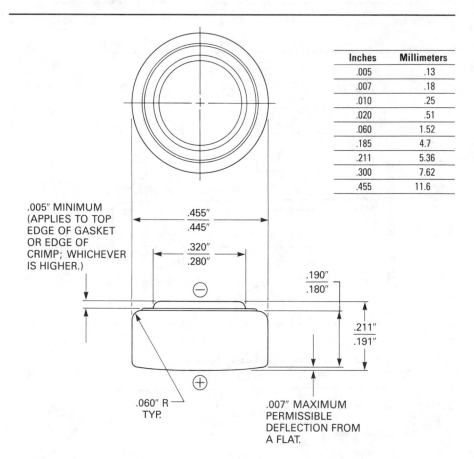

Inches	Millimeters
.005	.13
.007	.18
.010	.25
.020	.51
.060	1.52
.185	4.7
.211	5.36
.300	7.62
.455	11.6

.005" MINIMUM (APPLIES TO TOP EDGE OF GASKET OR EDGE OF CRIMP; WHICHEVER IS HIGHER.)

.455"
.445"

.320"
.280"

.190"
.180"

.211"
.191"

.060" R TYP.

.007" MAXIMUM PERMISSIBLE DEFLECTION FROM A FLAT.

Specifications

Voltage Taps	— , + 1.5
Average Service Capacity (to 0.9 volts) (Rated capacity at 6,500 ohm load)	190 milliampere-hours
Terminals	Flat Contacts
Average Weight	0.08 oz. (2.3 grams)
Volume (by displacement)	0.029 cubic inch (0.48 cubic centimeter)

Service data is on next page.

ENERCELL® Type 357

Preliminary Performance Data at 95°F (35°C)

Background: 94000 ohms continuous (IC simulated load 16.8 microamperes)
Pulse Width: 2 seconds
Pulse Frequency: 30 ohms @ 24/day (LED simulation)

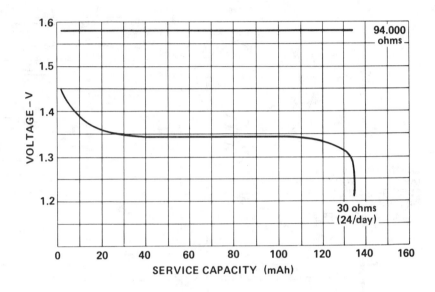

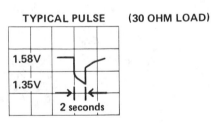

TYPICAL PULSE   (30 OHM LOAD)

Estimated Average Service at 95°F (35°C)

SCHEDULE	STARTING DRAIN (microamperes)	LOAD (ohms)	CUTOFF VOLTAGE 1.3V
24 hours/day	240	6,500	810 hours

Type: **Silver Oxide**
ANSI Designation: **WS10**
IEC Designation: **SR43**
Suggested Current Range: **0-10 milliamperes**

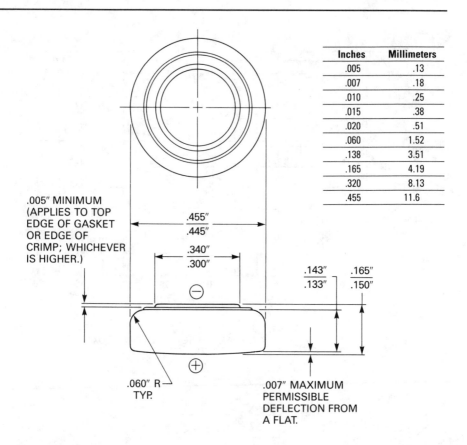

Inches	Millimeters
.005	.13
.007	.18
.010	.25
.015	.38
.020	.51
.060	1.52
.138	3.51
.165	4.19
.320	8.13
.455	11.6

.005" MINIMUM (APPLIES TO TOP EDGE OF GASKET OR EDGE OF CRIMP; WHICHEVER IS HIGHER.)

.455"
.445"

.340"
.300"

.143"
.133"

.165"
.150"

.060" R TYP.

.007" MAXIMUM PERMISSIBLE DEFLECTION FROM A FLAT.

Specifications

Voltage Taps	—, + 1.5
Average Service Capacity (to 0.9 volt) (Rated capacity at 6,500 ohm load)	120 milliampere-hours
Terminals	Flat Contacts
Average Weight	0.06 oz. (1.7 grams)
Volume (by displacement)	0.02 cubic inch (0.33 cubic centimeter)

Service data is on next page.

ENERCELL® Type 386

Preliminary Performance Data at 95°F (35°C)

Background: 94000 ohms continuous (IC simulated load 16.8 microamperes)
Pulse Width: 2 seconds
Pulse Frequency: 100 ohms @ 12/day (LCD backlight simulation)
30 ohms @ 24/day (LED simulation)

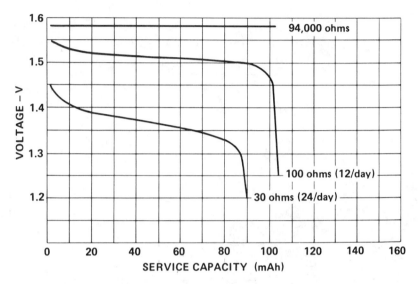

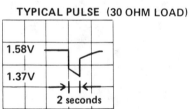

TYPICAL PULSE (30 OHM LOAD)

Estimated Average Service at 95°F (35°C)

SCHEDULE	STARTING DRAIN (microamperes)	LOAD (ohms)	CUTOFF VOLTAGE 1.3V
24 hours/day	240	6,500	510 hours

Type: **Silver Oxide**
IEC Designation: **SR55**
THIS BATTERY IS DESIGNED FOR USE ON CONTINUOUS
LOW DRAIN HIGH PULSE DRAIN ON DEMAND.

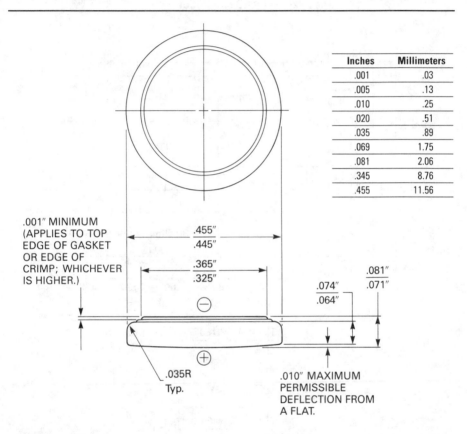

Inches	Millimeters
.001	.03
.005	.13
.010	.25
.020	.51
.035	.89
.069	1.75
.081	2.06
.345	8.76
.455	11.56

.001″ MINIMUM
(APPLIES TO TOP
EDGE OF GASKET
OR EDGE OF
CRIMP; WHICHEVER
IS HIGHER.)

.455″
.445″

.365″
.325″

.081″
.071″

.074″
.064″

⊖

⊕

.035R
Typ.

.010″ MAXIMUM
PERMISSIBLE
DEFLECTION FROM
A FLAT.

Specifications

Voltage Taps	—, + 1.5
Average Service Capacity (to 1.3 volts) (Rated capacity at 15,000 ohm load at 35° C)	43 milliampere-hours
Terminals	Flat Contacts
Average Weight	0.033 oz. (0.93 gram)
Volume	0.012 cubic inch (0.20 cubic centimeter)

Service data is on next page.

ENERCELL® Type 391

Estimated Average Service at 95°F (35°C)

SCHEDULE	STARTING DRAIN (microamperes)	LOAD (ohms)	CUTOFF VOLTAGE	
			0.9V	1.3V
24 hours/day	105	15,000	425 hours	415 hours
	10.6	150,000	175 days	170 days

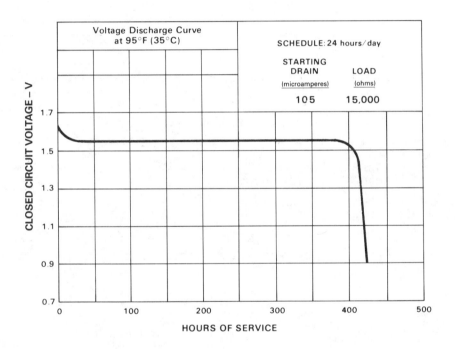

Internal Resistance

Closed circuit voltage no less than	1.2 volts
On a load of for 0.1 to 2 seconds	100 ohms

Type: **Silver Oxide**
THIS BATTERY IS DESIGNED FOR USE ON CONTINUOUS LOW DRAIN.

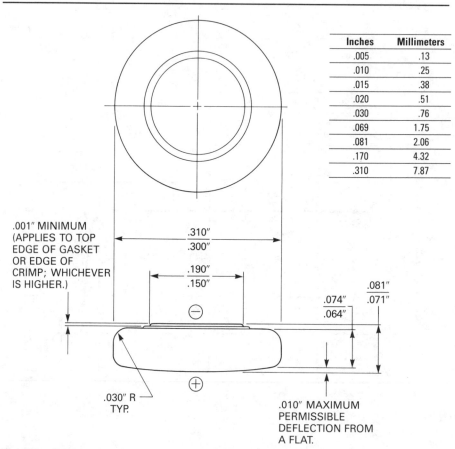

Inches	Millimeters
.005	.13
.010	.25
.015	.38
.020	.51
.030	.76
.069	1.75
.081	2.06
.170	4.32
.310	7.87

.001" MINIMUM (APPLIES TO TOP EDGE OF GASKET OR EDGE OF CRIMP; WHICHEVER IS HIGHER.)

.310"
.300"

.190"
.150"

.081"
.071"

.074"
.064"

.030" R
TYP.

.010" MAXIMUM PERMISSIBLE DEFLECTION FROM A FLAT.

Specifications

Voltage Taps	—, + 1.5
Average Service capacity (to 1.3 volts) (Rated capacity at 70,000 ohm load at 35°C)	18 milliampere-hours
Terminals	Flat Contacts
Average Weight	0.015 oz. (0.42 gram)
Volume	0.006 cubic inch (0.10 cubic centimeter)

Service data is on next page.

ENERCELL® Type 362

Estimated Average Service at 95°F (35°C)

SCHEDULE	STARTING DRAIN (microamperes)	LOAD (ohms)	CUTOFF VOLTAGE	
			0.9V	1.3V
24 hours/day	22	70,000	830 hours	820 hours

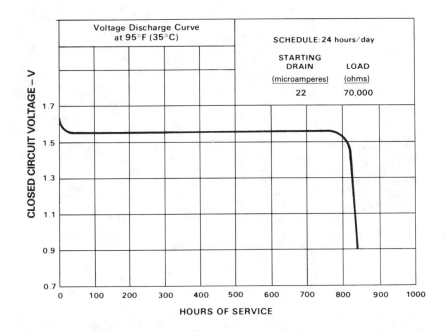

Internal Resistance

Closed circuit voltage no less than	0.75 volt
On a load of for 0.1 to 2 seconds	100 ohms

Type: **Silver Oxide**
THIS BATTERY IS DESIGNED FOR USE ON CONTINUOUS LOW
DRAIN.

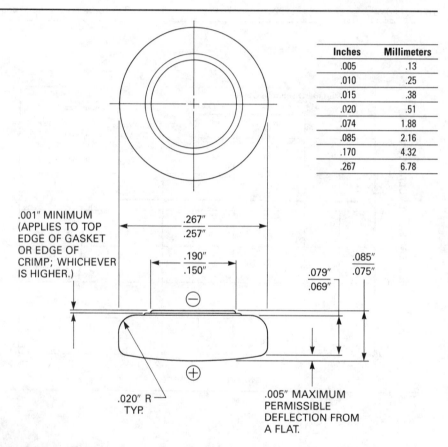

Inches	Millimeters
.005	.13
.010	.25
.015	.38
.020	.51
.074	1.88
.085	2.16
.170	4.32
.267	6.78

.001″ MINIMUM
(APPLIES TO TOP
EDGE OF GASKET
OR EDGE OF
CRIMP; WHICHEVER
IS HIGHER.)

.267″
.257″

.190″
.150″

.085″
.075″

.079″
.069″

⊖

⊕

.020″ R
TYP.

.005″ MAXIMUM
PERMISSIBLE
DEFLECTION FROM
A FLAT.

Specifications

Voltage Taps	— , + 1.5
Average Service Capacity (to 1.3 volts) (Rated capacity at 70,000 ohm load at 35°C)	15 milliampere-hours
Terminals	Flat Contacts
Average Weight	0.011 oz. (0.32 gram)
Volume	0.005 cubic inch (0.08 cubic centimeter)

Service data is on next page.

ENERCELL® Type 364

Estimated Average Service at 95°F (35°C)

SCHEDULE	STARTING DRAIN (microamperes)	LOAD (ohms)	CUTOFF VOLTAGE	
			0.9V	1.3V
24 hours/day	22	70,000	695 hours	680 hours
	2	750,000		295 days

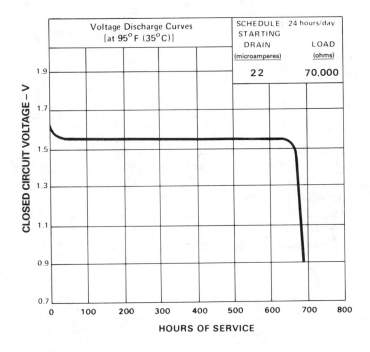

Voltage Discharge Curves [at 95°F (35°C)]

SCHEDULE: 24 hours/day

STARTING DRAIN (microamperes)	LOAD (ohms)
22	70,000

CLOSED CIRCUIT VOLTAGE – V

HOURS OF SERVICE

Internal Resistance

Closed circuit voltage no less than	0.75 volt
On a load of for 0.1 to 2 seconds	100 ohms

Type: **Silver Oxide**
THIS BATTERY IS DESIGNED FOR GENERAL ELECTRONIC
APPLICATIONS WHICH MAY REQUIRE HIGH RATE PULSES.

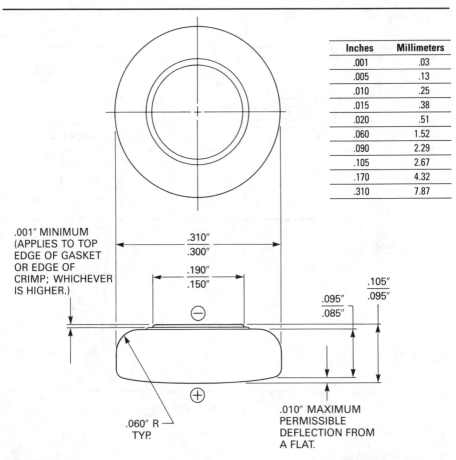

Inches	Millimeters
.001	.03
.005	.13
.010	.25
.015	.38
.020	.51
.060	1.52
.090	2.29
.105	2.67
.170	4.32
.310	7.87

.001" MINIMUM
(APPLIES TO TOP
EDGE OF GASKET
OR EDGE OF
CRIMP; WHICHEVER
IS HIGHER.)

.310"
.300"

.190"
.150"

.105"
.095"

.095"
.085"

⊖

⊕

.060" R
TYP.

.010" MAXIMUM
PERMISSIBLE
DEFLECTION FROM
A FLAT.

Specifications

Voltage Taps	—, + 1.5
Average Service Capacity (to 1.3 volts) (Rated capacity at 45,000 ohm load at 35°C)	24 milliampere-hours
Terminals	Flat Contacts
Average Weight	0.018 oz. (0.51 gram)
Volume	0.007 cubic inch (0.11 cubic centimeter)

Service data is on next page.

ENERCELL® Type 396

Estimated Average Service at 95°F (35°C)

SCHEDULE	STARTING DRAIN (microamperes)	LOAD (ohms)	CUTOFF VOLTAGE 1.3V
24 hours/day	35	45,000	699 hours
	2.5	650,000	475 days

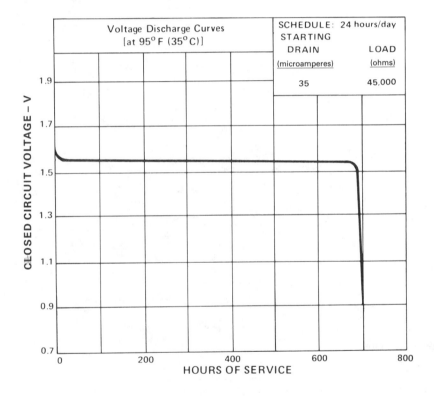

Internal Resistance

Closed circuit voltage no less than	1.05 volts
On a load of for 0.1 to 2 seconds	100 ohms

Type: **Silver Oxide**
IEC Designation: **SR57**
THIS BATTERY IS DESIGNED FOR USE ON CONTINUOUS LOW
DRAIN, HIGH PULSE DRAIN ON DEMAND.

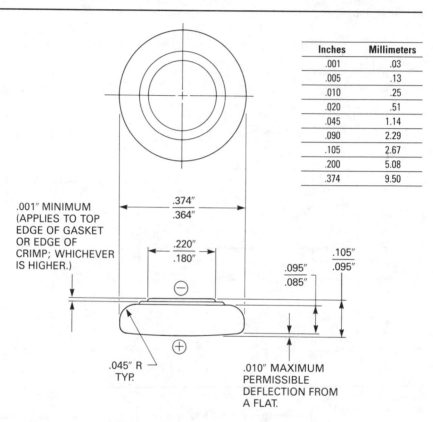

Inches	Millimeters
.001	.03
.005	.13
.010	.25
.020	.51
.045	1.14
.090	2.29
.105	2.67
.200	5.08
.374	9.50

.001" MINIMUM
(APPLIES TO TOP
EDGE OF GASKET
OR EDGE OF
CRIMP; WHICHEVER
IS HIGHER.)

.374"
.364"

.220"
.180"

.105"
.095"
.095"
.085"

.045" R
TYP.

.010" MAXIMUM
PERMISSIBLE
DEFLECTION FROM
A FLAT.

Specifications

Voltage Taps	—, + 1.5
Average Service Capacity (to 1.3 volts) (Rated capacity at 20,000 ohm load at 35°C)	40 milliampere-hours
Terminals	Flat Contacts
Average Weight	0.029 oz. (0.79 gram)
Volume	0.011 cubic inch (0.18 cubic centimeter)

Service data is on next page.

ENERCELL® Type 399

Estimated Average Service at 95°F (35°C)

SCHEDULE	STARTING DRAIN (microamperes)	LOAD (ohms)	CUTOFF VOLTAGE 1.3V
24 hours/day	78.5	20,000	520 hours
	4.5	350,000	370 days

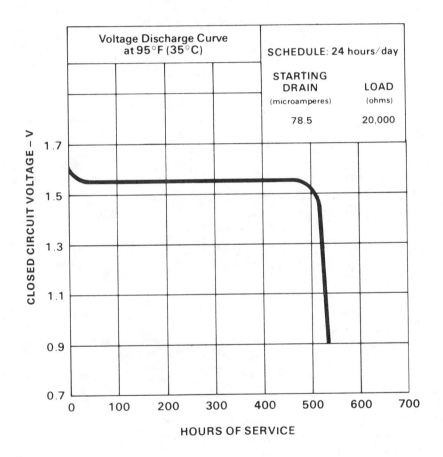

HOURS OF SERVICE

Internal Resistance

Closed circuit voltage no less than	1.1 volts
On a load of for 0.1 to 2 seconds	100 ohms

ENERCELL® Type 390

Type: **Silver Oxide**
ANSI/NEDA Designation: **1159SO**
IEC Designation: **SR54**
Suggested Current Range: **See Discharge Data**

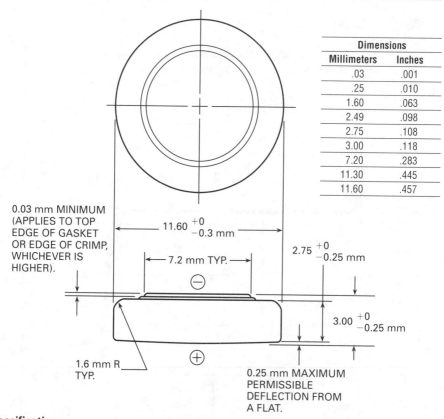

Dimensions	
Millimeters	Inches
.03	.001
.25	.010
1.60	.063
2.49	.098
2.75	.108
3.00	.118
7.20	.283
11.30	.445
11.60	.457

0.03 mm MINIMUM (APPLIES TO TOP EDGE OF GASKET OR EDGE OF CRIMP, WHICHEVER IS HIGHER).

11.60 $^{+0}_{-0.3}$ mm

7.2 mm TYP.

2.75 $^{+0}_{-0.25}$ mm

3.00 $^{+0}_{-0.25}$ mm

1.6 mm R TYP.

0.25 mm MAXIMUM PERMISSIBLE DEFLECTION FROM A FLAT.

Specifications

Voltage Taps	−, + 1.5
Average Service Capacity (to 1.3V) (Rated Capacity at 15,000 ohms load at 21.1°C)	85mAh
Terminals	Flat Contacts
Average Weight	1.35 grams (0.048 oz.)
Volume	0.32 cubic centimeter (0.019 cubic inch)

Service data is on the next page.

ENERCELL® Type 390

Estimated Average Service at 70°F (21.1°C)

SCHEDULE	STARTING DRAIN (microamperes)	LOAD (ohms)	CUTOFF VOLTAGE 1.3V
24 hours/day	130	15,000	825 hours

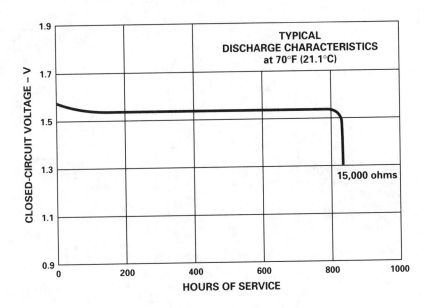

TYPICAL DISCHARGE CHARACTERISTICS at 70°F (21.1°C)

15,000 ohms

CLOSED-CIRCUIT VOLTAGE – V

HOURS OF SERVICE

Internal Resistance

Closed-circuit voltage no less than	0.9 volt
on a load of for 0.1 to 2.0 seconds	100 ohms

Typical Closed-Circuit Voltage

During discharge on a load of for 0.0078 seconds	2,000 ohms

TEMPERATURE	DEPTH OF DISCHARGE AS PERCENT OF RATED CAPACITY		
	0%	40%	80%
70°F (21.1°C)	1.57V	1.56V	1.56V
14°F (−10°C)	1.45V	1.49V	1.51V

Type: **Silver Oxide**
Suggested Current Range: **See Discharge Data**

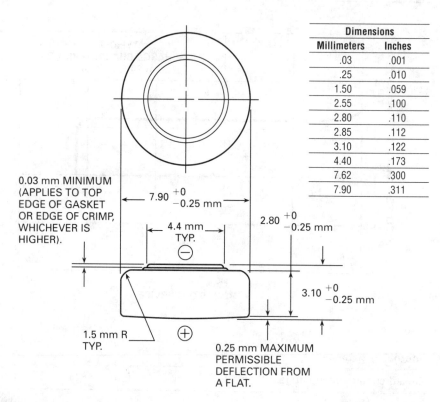

Dimensions	
Millimeters	Inches
.03	.001
.25	.010
1.50	.059
2.55	.100
2.80	.110
2.85	.112
3.10	.122
4.40	.173
7.62	.300
7.90	.311

0.03 mm MINIMUM
(APPLIES TO TOP
EDGE OF GASKET
OR EDGE OF CRIMP,
WHICHEVER IS
HIGHER).

7.90 $^{+0}_{-0.25}$ mm

4.4 mm
TYP.

$\ominus$

2.80 $^{+0}_{-0.25}$ mm

3.10 $^{+0}_{-0.25}$ mm

1.5 mm R
TYP.

$\oplus$

0.25 mm MAXIMUM
PERMISSIBLE
DEFLECTION FROM
A FLAT.

Specifications

Voltage Taps	$-, + 1.5$
Average Service Capacity (to 1.3V) (Rated Capacity at 20,000 ohms load at 21.1°C)	36mAh
Terminals	Flat Contacts
Average Weight	0.57 gram (0.02 oz.)
Volume	0.15 cubic centimeter (0.009 cubic inch)

Service data is on the next page.

ENERCELL® Type 329

Estimated Average Service at 70°F (21.1°C)

SCHEDULE	STARTING DRAIN (microamperes)	LOAD (ohms)	CUTOFF VOLTAGE 1.3V
24 hours/day	77.5	20,000	465 hours

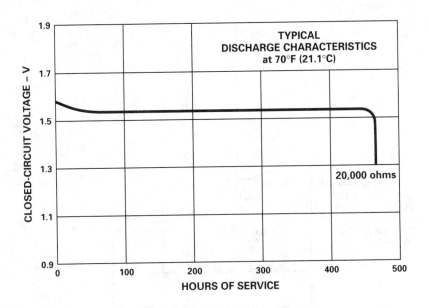

TYPICAL DISCHARGE CHARACTERISTICS at 70°F (21.1°C)

20,000 ohms

CLOSED-CIRCUIT VOLTAGE – V

HOURS OF SERVICE

Internal Resistance

Closed-circuit voltage no less than	0.9 volt
on a load of for 0.1 to 2.0 seconds	100 ohms

Typical Closed-Circuit Voltage

During discharge on a load of for 0.0078 seconds	2,000 ohms

TEMPERATURE	DEPTH OF DISCHARGE AS PERCENT OF RATED CAPACITY		
	0%	40%	80%
70°F (21.1°C)	1.58V	1.54V	1.55V
14°F (−10°C)	1.47V	1.37V	1.40V

Type: **Silver Oxide**
ANSI/NEDA Designation: **1171S0**
IEC Designation: **SR69**
Suggested Current Range: **See Discharge Data**

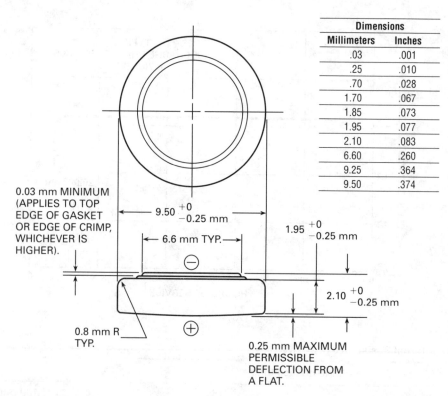

Dimensions	
Millimeters	**Inches**
.03	.001
.25	.010
.70	.028
1.70	.067
1.85	.073
1.95	.077
2.10	.083
6.60	.260
9.25	.364
9.50	.374

0.03 mm MINIMUM
(APPLIES TO TOP
EDGE OF GASKET
OR EDGE OF CRIMP,
WHICHEVER IS
HIGHER).

9.50 $^{+0}_{-0.25}$ mm

← 6.6 mm TYP. →

1.95 $^{+0}_{-0.25}$ mm

2.10 $^{+0}_{-0.25}$ mm

0.8 mm R
TYP.

0.25 mm MAXIMUM
PERMISSIBLE
DEFLECTION FROM
A FLAT.

Specifications

Voltage Taps	−, + 1.5
Average Service Capacity (to 1.3V) (Rated Capacity at 45,000 ohms load at 21.1°C)	35mAh
Terminals	Flat Contacts
Average Weight	0.66 gram (0.023 oz.)
Volume	0.15 cubic centimeter (0.009 cubic inch)

Service data is on the next page.

ENERCELL® Type 371

Estimated Average Service at 70°F (21.1°C)

SCHEDULE	STARTING DRAIN (microamperes)	LOAD (ohms)	CUTOFF VOLTAGE 1.3V
24 hours/day	34.4	45,000	1,016 hours

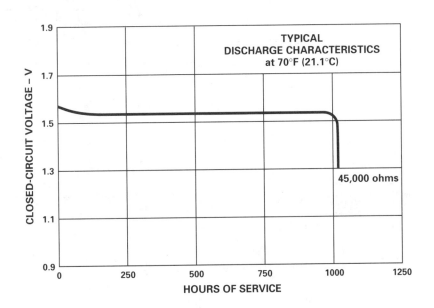

TYPICAL DISCHARGE CHARACTERISTICS at 70°F (21.1°C)

45,000 ohms

CLOSED-CIRCUIT VOLTAGE – V

HOURS OF SERVICE

Internal Resistance

Closed-circuit voltage no less than	1.1 volts
on a load of for 0.1 to 2.0 seconds	100 ohms

Typical Closed-Circuit Voltage

During discharge on a load of   2,000 ohms
for 0.0078 seconds

TEMPERATURE	DEPTH OF DISCHARGE AS PERCENT OF RATED CAPACITY		
	0%	40%	80%
70°F (21.1°C)	1.59V	1.56V	1.56V
14°F (−10°C)	1.53V	1.49V	1.50V

Type: **Silver Oxide**
ANSI/NEDA Designation: **1176SO**
IEC Designation: **SR66**
Suggested Current Range: **See Discharge Data**

Dimensions	
Millimeters	**Inches**
.03	.001
.13	.005
.20	.008
.90	.035
2.31	.091
2.40	.094
2.57	.101
2.60	.102
4.30	.169
6.55	.258
6.80	.268

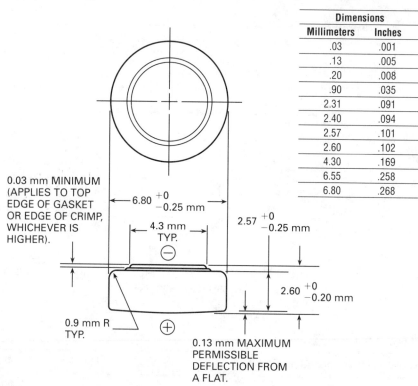

0.03 mm MINIMUM
(APPLIES TO TOP
EDGE OF GASKET
OR EDGE OF CRIMP,
WHICHEVER IS
HIGHER).

$6.80 \begin{smallmatrix} +0 \\ -0.25 \end{smallmatrix}$ mm

4.3 mm
TYP.

$2.57 \begin{smallmatrix} +0 \\ -0.25 \end{smallmatrix}$ mm

$2.60 \begin{smallmatrix} +0 \\ -0.20 \end{smallmatrix}$ mm

0.9 mm R
TYP.

0.13 mm MAXIMUM
PERMISSIBLE
DEFLECTION FROM
A FLAT.

Specifications

Voltage Taps	−, + 1.5
Average Service Capacity (to 1.3V) (Rated Capacity at 45,000 ohms load at 21.1°C)	28mAh
Terminals	Flat Contacts
Average Weight	0.42 gram (0.015 oz.)
Volume	0.09 cubic centimeter (0.006 cubic inch)

Service data is on the next page.

ENERCELL® Type 377

Estimated Average Service at 70°F (21.1°C)

SCHEDULE	STARTING DRAIN (microamperes)	LOAD (ohms)	CUTOFF VOLTAGE 1.3V
24 hours/day	34.4	45,000	813 hours

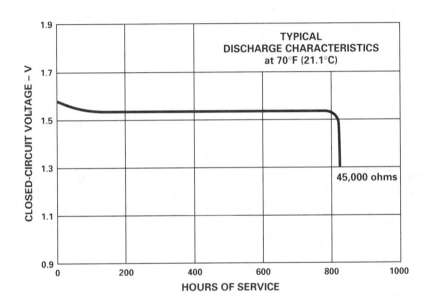

TYPICAL DISCHARGE CHARACTERISTICS at 70°F (21.1°C)

45,000 ohms

CLOSED-CIRCUIT VOLTAGE – V

HOURS OF SERVICE

Internal Resistance

Closed-circuit voltage no less than	0.9 volt
on a load of for 0.1 to 2.0 seconds	100 ohms

Typical Closed-Circuit Voltage

During discharge on a load of for 0.0078 seconds	2,000 ohms

TEMPERATURE	DEPTH OF DISCHARGE AS PERCENT OF RATED CAPACITY		
	0%	40%	80%
70°F (21.1°C)	1.58V	1.55V	1.55V
14°F (−10°C)	1.48V	1.37V	1.35V

Type: **Silver Oxide**
ANSI/NEDA Designation: **1134SO**
IEC Designation: **SR41**
Suggested Current Range: **See Discharge Data**

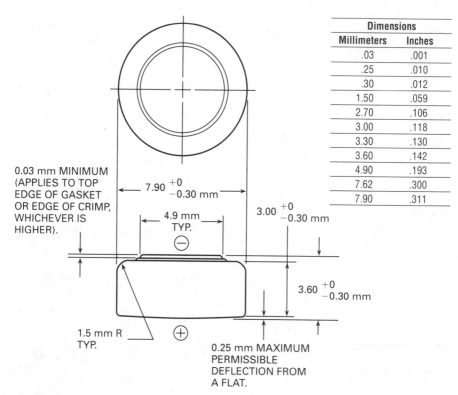

Dimensions	
Millimeters	Inches
.03	.001
.25	.010
.30	.012
1.50	.059
2.70	.106
3.00	.118
3.30	.130
3.60	.142
4.90	.193
7.62	.300
7.90	.311

0.03 mm MINIMUM
(APPLIES TO TOP
EDGE OF GASKET
OR EDGE OF CRIMP,
WHICHEVER IS
HIGHER).

$7.90 \begin{smallmatrix} +0 \\ -0.30 \end{smallmatrix}$ mm

4.9 mm
TYP.

$3.00 \begin{smallmatrix} +0 \\ -0.30 \end{smallmatrix}$ mm

$3.60 \begin{smallmatrix} +0 \\ -0.30 \end{smallmatrix}$ mm

1.5 mm R
TYP.

0.25 mm MAXIMUM
PERMISSIBLE
DEFLECTION FROM
A FLAT.

Specifications

Voltage Taps	−, + 1.5
Average Service Capacity (to 1.3V) (Rated Capacity at 15,000 ohms load at 21.1°C)	43mAh
Terminals	Flat Contacts
Average Weight	0.57 gram (0.020 oz.)
Volume	0.18 cubic centimeter (0.011 cubic inch)

Service data is on the next page.

ENERCELL® Type 384

Estimated Average Service at 70°F (21.1°C)

SCHEDULE	STARTING DRAIN (microamperes)	LOAD (ohms)	CUTOFF VOLTAGE 1.3V
24 hours/day	103	15,000	416 hours

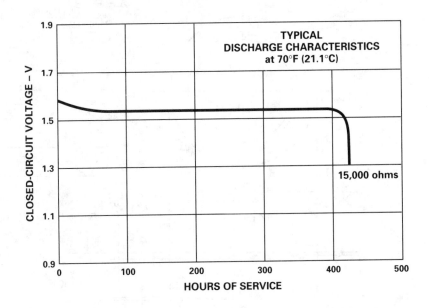

TYPICAL DISCHARGE CHARACTERISTICS at 70°F (21.1°C)

15,000 ohms

CLOSED-CIRCUIT VOLTAGE – V

HOURS OF SERVICE

Internal Resistance

Closed-circuit voltage no less than	1.0 volt
on a load of for 0.1 to 2.0 seconds	100 ohms

Typical Closed-Circuit Voltage

During discharge on a load of for 0.0078 seconds — 2,000 ohms

TEMPERATURE	DEPTH OF DISCHARGE AS PERCENT OF RATED CAPACITY		
	0%	40%	80%
70°F (21.1°C)	1.57V	1.55V	1.54V
14°F (−10°C)	1.44V	1.43V	1.43V

Type: **Silver Oxide**
ANSI/NEDA Designation: **1162SO**
IEC Designation: **SR57/TR57**
Suggested Current Range: **See Discharge Data**

Dimensions	
Millimeters	Inches
.03	.001
.25	.010
.30	.012
.70	.028
2.16	.085
2.41	.095
2.70	.106
6.60	.260
9.25	.364
9.50	.374

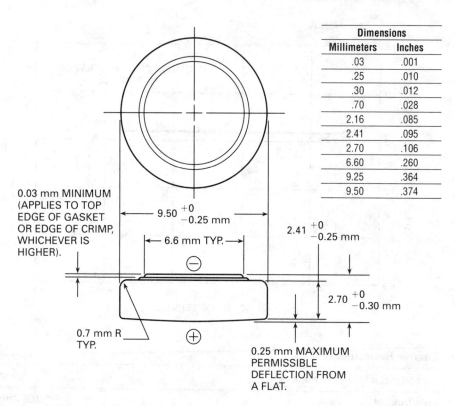

0.03 mm MINIMUM
(APPLIES TO TOP
EDGE OF GASKET
OR EDGE OF CRIMP,
WHICHEVER IS
HIGHER).

9.50 $^{+0}_{-0.25}$ mm

2.41 $^{+0}_{-0.25}$ mm

6.6 mm TYP.

2.70 $^{+0}_{-0.30}$ mm

0.7 mm R
TYP.

0.25 mm MAXIMUM
PERMISSIBLE
DEFLECTION FROM
A FLAT.

Specifications

Voltage Taps	−, + 1.5
Average Service Capacity (to 1.3V) (Rated Capacity at 20,000 ohms load at 21.1°C)	53mAh
Terminals	Flat Contacts
Average Weight	0.79 gram (0.029 oz.)
Volume	0.19 cubic centimeter (0.012 cubic inch)

Service data is on the next page.

ENERCELL® Type 395

Estimated Average Service at 70°F (21.1°C)

SCHEDULE	STARTING DRAIN (microamperes)	LOAD (ohms)	CUTOFF VOLTAGE 1.3V
24 hours/day	77.5	20,000	685 hours

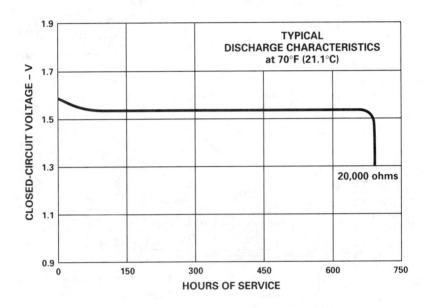

TYPICAL
DISCHARGE CHARACTERISTICS
at 70°F (21.1°C)

20,000 ohms

CLOSED-CIRCUIT VOLTAGE – V

HOURS OF SERVICE

Internal Resistance

Closed-circuit voltage no less than	1.1 volts
on a load of for 0.1 to 2.0 seconds	100 ohms

Typical Closed-Circuit Voltage

During discharge on a load of for 0.0078 seconds	2,000 ohms

TEMPERATURE	DEPTH OF DISCHARGE AS PERCENT OF RATED CAPACITY		
	0%	40%	80%
70°F (21.1°C)	1.58V	1.56V	1.56V
14°F (−10°C)	1.55V	1.45V	1.46V

ENERCELL® Type 397

Type: **Silver Oxide**
ANSI/NEDA Designation: **1164SO**
IEC Designation: **SR59**
Suggested Current Range: **See Discharge Data**

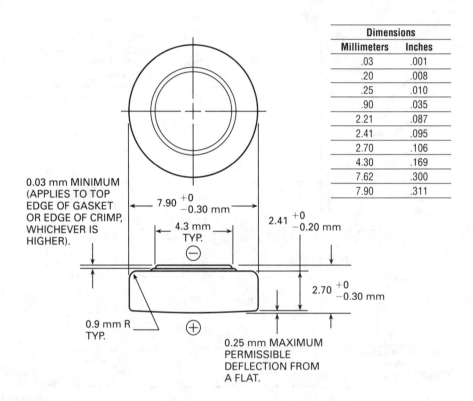

Dimensions	
Millimeters	Inches
.03	.001
.20	.008
.25	.010
.90	.035
2.21	.087
2.41	.095
2.70	.106
4.30	.169
7.62	.300
7.90	.311

0.03 mm MINIMUM (APPLIES TO TOP EDGE OF GASKET OR EDGE OF CRIMP, WHICHEVER IS HIGHER).

$7.90 \, {}^{+0}_{-0.30}$ mm

4.3 mm TYP.

$2.41 \, {}^{+0}_{-0.20}$ mm

$2.70 \, {}^{+0}_{-0.30}$ mm

0.9 mm R TYP.

0.25 mm MAXIMUM PERMISSIBLE DEFLECTION FROM A FLAT.

Specifications

Voltage Taps	−, + 1.5
Average Service Capacity (to 1.3V) (Rated Capacity at 45,000 ohms load at 21.1°C)	37mAh
Terminals	Flat Contacts
Average Weight	0.51 gram (0.018 oz.)
Volume	0.13 cubic centimeter (0.008 cubic inch)

Service data is on the next page.

ENERCELL® Type 397

Estimated Average Service at 70°F (21.1°C)

SCHEDULE	STARTING DRAIN (microamperes)	LOAD (ohms)	CUTOFF VOLTAGE 1.3V
24 hours/day	34.4	45,000	1,074 hours

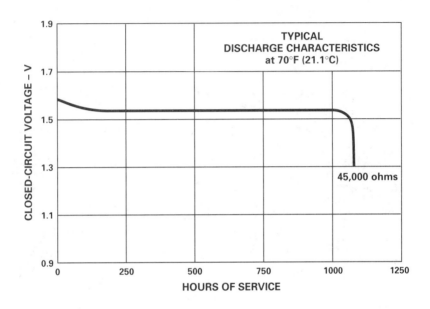

TYPICAL
DISCHARGE CHARACTERISTICS
at 70°F (21.1°C)

45,000 ohms

CLOSED-CIRCUIT VOLTAGE – V

HOURS OF SERVICE

Internal Resistance

Closed-circuit voltage no less than	0.9 volt
on a load of for 0.1 to 2.0 seconds	100 ohms

Typical Closed-Circuit Voltage

During discharge on a load of for 0.0078 seconds	2,000 ohms

TEMPERATURE	DEPTH OF DISCHARGE AS PERCENT OF RATED CAPACITY 0%	40%	80%
70°F (21.1°C)	1.58V	1.56V	1.56V
14°F (−10°C)	1.45V	1.37V	1.41V

Type: **Silver Oxide**
ANSI/NEDA Designation: **1186SO**
Suggested Current Range: **See Discharge Data**

Dimensions	
Millimeters	Inches
.10	.004
.13	.005
.20	.008
.90	.035
2.20	.087
2.40	.094
2.50	.098
2.70	.106
3.90	.154
5.65	.222
5.80	.228

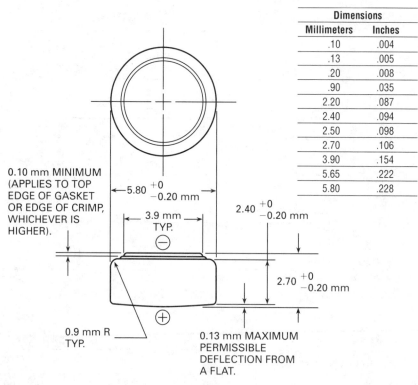

0.10 mm MINIMUM (APPLIES TO TOP EDGE OF GASKET OR EDGE OF CRIMP, WHICHEVER IS HIGHER).

5.80 $^{+0}_{-0.20}$ mm

3.9 mm TYP.

2.40 $^{+0}_{-0.20}$ mm

2.70 $^{+0}_{-0.20}$ mm

0.9 mm R TYP.

0.13 mm MAXIMUM PERMISSIBLE DEFLECTION FROM A FLAT.

Specifications

Voltage Taps	−, + 1.5
Average Service Capacity (to 1.3V) (Rated Capacity at 70,000 ohms load at 21.1°C)	16mAh
Terminals	Flat Contacts
Average Weight	0.31 gram (0.011 oz.)
Volume	0.07 cubic centimeter (0.004 cubic inch)

Service data is on the next page.

ENERCELL® Type 319

Estimated Average Service at 70°F (21.1°C)

SCHEDULE	STARTING DRAIN (microamperes)	LOAD (ohms)	CUTOFF VOLTAGE 1.3V
24 hours/day	22.1	70,000	723 hours

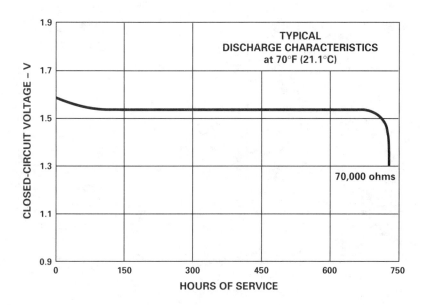

TYPICAL
DISCHARGE CHARACTERISTICS
at 70°F (21.1°C)

70,000 ohms

CLOSED-CIRCUIT VOLTAGE – V

HOURS OF SERVICE

Internal Resistance

Closed-circuit voltage no less than	0.8 volt
on a load of for 0.1 to 2.0 seconds	100 ohms

Typical Closed-Circuit Voltage

During discharge on a load of for 0.0078 seconds	2,000 ohms

	DEPTH OF DISCHARGE AS PERCENT OF RATED CAPACITY		
TEMPERATURE	0%	40%	80%
70°F (21.1°C)	1.58V	1.54V	1.53V
14°F (−10°C)	1.40V	1.25V	1.28V

ENERCELL® Type 379

Type: **Silver Oxide**
ANSI Designation: **1191SO**
Suggested Current Range: **See Discharge Data**

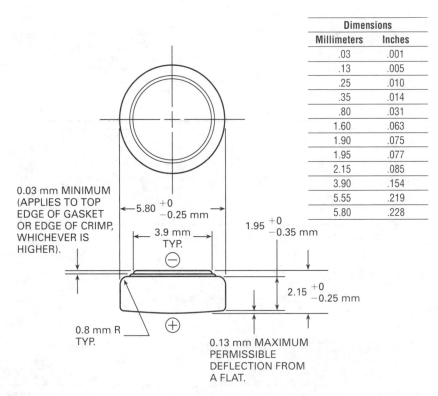

Dimensions	
Millimeters	Inches
.03	.001
.13	.005
.25	.010
.35	.014
.80	.031
1.60	.063
1.90	.075
1.95	.077
2.15	.085
3.90	.154
5.55	.219
5.80	.228

0.03 mm MINIMUM (APPLIES TO TOP EDGE OF GASKET OR EDGE OF CRIMP, WHICHEVER IS HIGHER).

5.80 $^{+0}_{-0.25}$ mm

3.9 mm TYP.

1.95 $^{+0}_{-0.35}$ mm

2.15 $^{+0}_{-0.25}$ mm

0.8 mm R TYP.

0.13 mm MAXIMUM PERMISSIBLE DEFLECTION FROM A FLAT.

Specifications

Voltage Taps	−, + 1.5
Average Service Capacity (to 1.3V) (Rated Capacity at 70,000 ohms load at 21.1°C)	14mAh
Terminals	Flat Contacts
Average Weight	0.25 gram (0.009 oz.)
Volume	0.06 cubic centimeter (0.003 cubic inch)

Service data is on the next page.

ENERCELL® Type 379

Estimated Average Service at 70°F (21.1°C)

SCHEDULE	STARTING DRAIN (microamperes)	LOAD (ohms)	CUTOFF VOLTAGE 1.3V
24 hours/day	22.1	70,000	632 hours

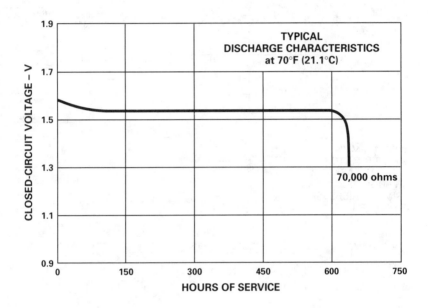

Internal Resistance

Closed-circuit voltage no less than	0.8 volt
on a load of for 0.1 to 2.0 seconds	100 ohms

Typical Closed-Circuit Voltage

During discharge on a load of   2,000 ohms
    for 0.0078 seconds

	DEPTH OF DISCHARGE AS PERCENT OF RATED CAPACITY		
TEMPERATURE	0%	40%	80%
70°F (21.1°C)	1.58V	1.54V	1.54V
14°F (−10°C)	1.43V	1.36V	1.33V

Type: **Mercuric Oxide**
ANSI Designation: **WM6**
IEC Designation: **MR48**
Suggested Current Range: **0-100 microamperes**

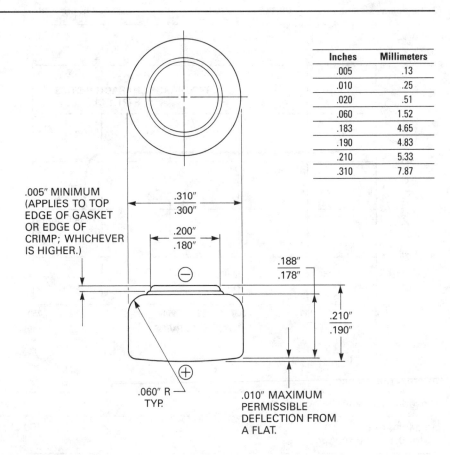

Inches	Millimeters
.005	.13
.010	.25
.020	.51
.060	1.52
.183	4.65
.190	4.83
.210	5.33
.310	7.87

.005" MINIMUM (APPLIES TO TOP EDGE OF GASKET OR EDGE OF CRIMP; WHICHEVER IS HIGHER.)

.310"
.300"

.200"
.180"

.188"
.178"

.210"
.190"

.060" R TYP.

.010" MAXIMUM PERMISSIBLE DEFLECTION FROM A FLAT.

Specifications

Voltage Taps	—, + 1.35
Average Service Capacity (to 1.2 volts) (Rated capacity at 13,000 ohm load)	95 milliampere-hours
Terminals	Flat Contacts
Average Weight	0.05 oz. (1.42 grams)
Volume (by displacement)	0.015 cubic inch (0.25 cubic centimeter)

Service data is on next page.

ENERCELL® Type 323

Estimated Average Service at 70°F (21.1°C)

SCHEDULE	STARTING DRAIN (microamperes)	LOAD (ohms)	CUTOFF VOLTAGE
			1.2V
24 hours/day	104	13,000	950 hours
	10.3	130,000	13 months

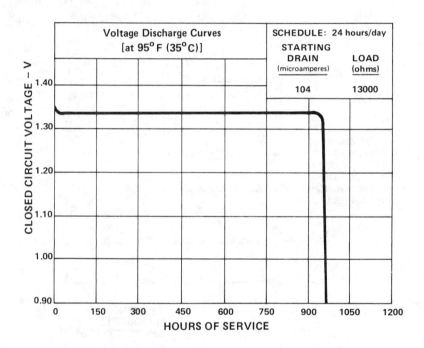

Voltage Discharge Curves [at 95° F (35°C)]

SCHEDULE: 24 hours/day

STARTING DRAIN (microamperes)	LOAD (ohms)
104	13000

IMPEDANCE

Approximate open circuit impedance at 1000 Hz: 65 ohms average

Type: **Mercuric Oxide**
ANSI Designation: **WM10**
IEC Designation: **MR42**
Suggested Current Range: **0-100 microamperes**

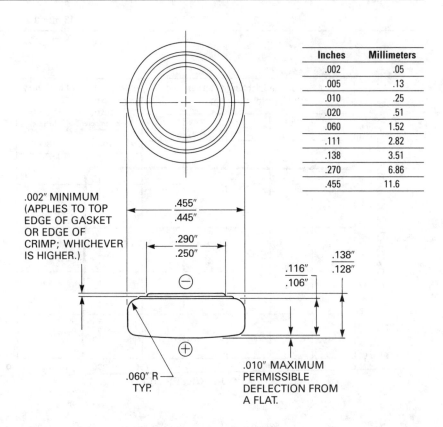

Inches	Millimeters
.002	.05
.005	.13
.010	.25
.020	.51
.060	1.52
.111	2.82
.138	3.51
.270	6.86
.455	11.6

.002" MINIMUM
(APPLIES TO TOP
EDGE OF GASKET
OR EDGE OF
CRIMP; WHICHEVER
IS HIGHER.)

.455"
.445"

.290"
.250"

.138"
.128"

.116"
.106"

⊖

⊕

.060" R
TYP.

.010" MAXIMUM
PERMISSIBLE
DEFLECTION FROM
A FLAT.

Specifications

Voltage Taps	—, + 1.35
Average Service Capacity (to 1.2 volts) (Rated capacity at 13,000 ohm load)	120 milliampere-hours
Terminals	Flat Contacts
Average Weight	0.06 oz. (1.7 grams)
Volume (by displacement)	0.019 cubic inch (0.31 cubic centimeter)

Service data is on next page.

ENERCELL® Type 343

Estimated Average Service at 95°F (35°C)

SCHEDULE	STARTING DRAIN (microamperes)	LOAD (ohms)	CUTOFF VOLTAGE	
			0.9V	1.2V
24 hours/day	104	13,000	1200 hours	1170 hours
	10.3	130,000	16 months (estimated)	15.8 months (estimated)

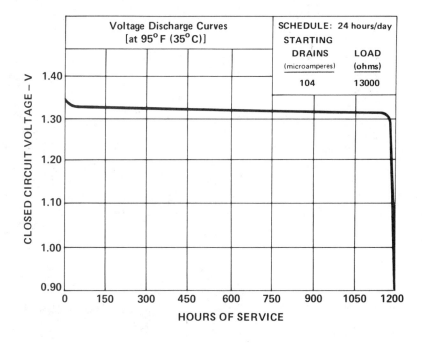

IMPEDANCE

Approximate open circuit impedance at 1000 Hz: 80 ohms average

Type: **Mercuric Oxide**
ANSI Designation: **N15**
IEC Designation: **NR44**

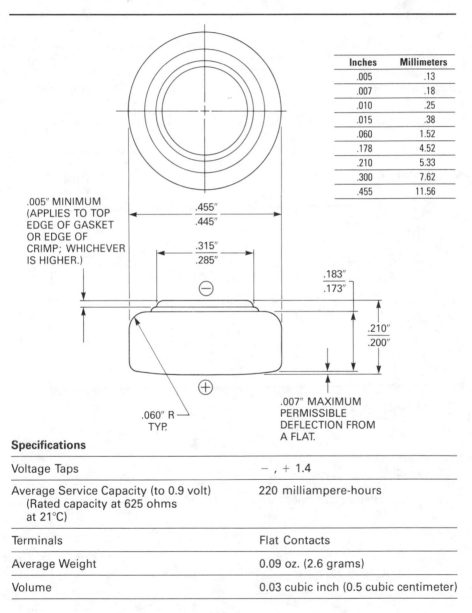

Inches	Millimeters
.005	.13
.007	.18
.010	.25
.015	.38
.060	1.52
.178	4.52
.210	5.33
.300	7.62
.455	11.56

.005″ MINIMUM (APPLIES TO TOP EDGE OF GASKET OR EDGE OF CRIMP; WHICHEVER IS HIGHER.)

.455″
.445″

.315″
.285″

⊖

.183″
.173″

.210″
.200″

⊕

.060″ R
TYP.

.007″ MAXIMUM PERMISSIBLE DEFLECTION FROM A FLAT.

Specifications

Voltage Taps	− , + 1.4
Average Service Capacity (to 0.9 volt) (Rated capacity at 625 ohms at 21°C)	220 milliampere-hours
Terminals	Flat Contacts
Average Weight	0.09 oz. (2.6 grams)
Volume	0.03 cubic inch (0.5 cubic centimeter)

Service data is on next page.

ENERCELL® Type P675M

Estimated Average Hours Service at 70°F (21°C)

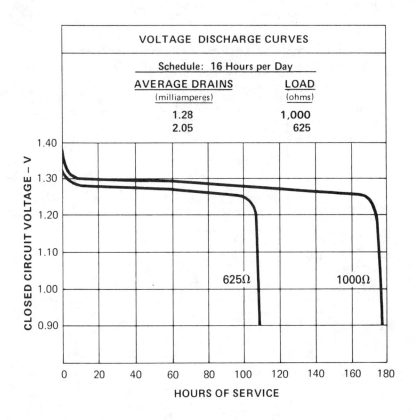

VOLTAGE DISCHARGE CURVES

Schedule: 16 Hours per Day

AVERAGE DRAINS (milliamperes)	LOAD (ohms)
1.28	1,000
2.05	625

Impedance

The impedance of these cells on open circuit and during useful discharge typically varies from 3–12 ohms. This applies over a frequency range of 40–5000 hertz and at the current drains shown above.

Service vs. Temperature

For following conditions:

Average Drains:	1.28 and 2.05 milliamperes
Loads:	1,000 and 625 ohms
Discharge Schedule:	16 hours/day

Temperature	% of 70°F Service vs. Temperature	
	0.9V	1.2V
70°F (21°C)	100	100
40°F (4.4°C)	95	70

Type: **Mercuric Oxide**
ANSI Designation: **N6**
IEC Designation: **NR48**

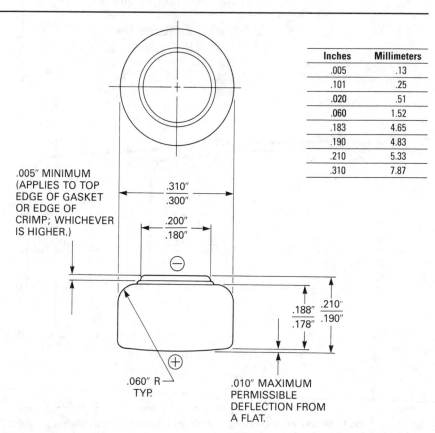

Inches	Millimeters
.005	.13
.101	.25
.020	.51
.060	1.52
.183	4.65
.190	4.83
.210	5.33
.310	7.87

.005" MINIMUM
(APPLIES TO TOP
EDGE OF GASKET
OR EDGE OF
CRIMP; WHICHEVER
IS HIGHER.)

.310"
.300"

.200"
.180"

.188" .210"
.178" .190"

.060" R
TYP.

.010" MAXIMUM
PERMISSIBLE
DEFLECTION FROM
A FLAT.

Specifications

Voltage Taps	—, + 1.4
Average Service Capacity (to 0.9 volt) (Rated capacity at 1,500 ohms at 21.1° C)	85 milliampere-hours
Terminals	Flat Contacts
Average Weight	0.04 oz. (1.1 grams)
Volume	0.02 cubic inch (0.3 cubic centimeter)

Service data is on next page.

ENERCELL® Type 13M

Estimated Average Hours Service at 70°F (21.1°C)

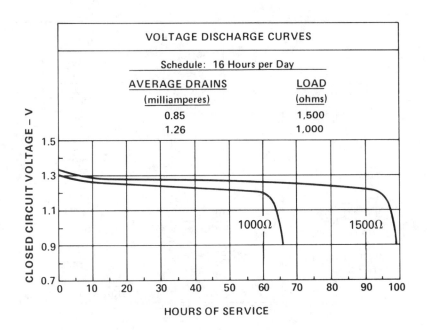

Impedance

The impedance of these cells on open circuit and during useful discharge typically varies from 3–12 ohms. This applies over a frequency range of 40–5000 hertz and at the current drains shown above.

Service vs. Temperature

For following conditions:

Average Drains:	1.28 and 2.05 milliamperes
Loads:	1,000 and 625 ohms
Discharge Schedule:	16 hours/day

	% of 70°F Service vs. Temperature	
Temperature	0.9V	1.2V
70°F (21.1°C)	100	100
40°F (4.4°C)	95	70

Type: **Mercuric Oxide**
ANSI Designation: **M5**
Suggested Current Range: **0-5 milliamperes**

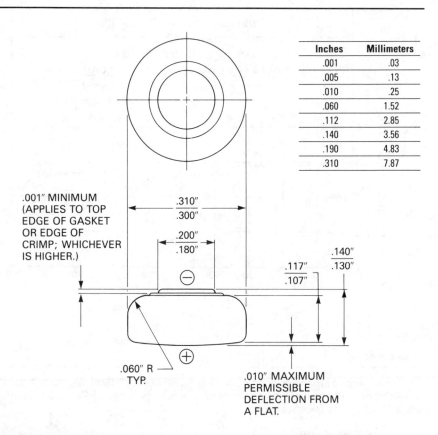

Inches	Millimeters
.001	.03
.005	.13
.010	.25
.060	1.52
.112	2.85
.140	3.56
.190	4.83
.310	7.87

.001" MINIMUM (APPLIES TO TOP EDGE OF GASKET OR EDGE OF CRIMP; WHICHEVER IS HIGHER.)

.310"
.300"

.200"
.180"

.140"
.130"

.117"
.107"

.060" R TYP.

.010" MAXIMUM PERMISSIBLE DEFLECTION FROM A FLAT.

Specifications

Voltage Taps	— , + 1.4
Average Service Capacity (to 0.9 volt) (Rated capacity at 0.85 milliampere)	45 milliampere-hours
Terminals	Flat Contacts
Average Weight	0.03 oz. (0.85 grams)
Volume (by displacement)	0.008 cubic inch (0.13 cubic centimeter)

Service data is on next page.

ENERCELL® Type 312M

Estimated Average Hours Service at 70°F (21.1°C)

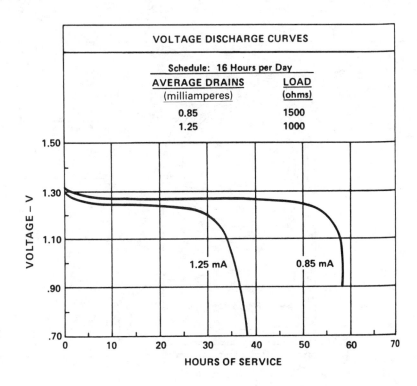

Impedance

The impedance of these cells on open circuit and during useful discharge typically varies from 5–20 ohms. This applies over a frequency range of 40–10,000 hertz and at the current drains shown above.

Service vs. Temperature

For following conditions:

Starting Drain:	0.7 milliampere
Load:	2000 ohms
Discharge Schedule:	16 hours/day

	% of 70°F Service vs. Temperature	
Temperature	0.9V	1.2V
70°F	100	100
40°F	95	70

ENERCELL® Type CR2016H

Type: **Lithium-Manganese Dioxide**
Suggested Current Range: **See Discharge Data**

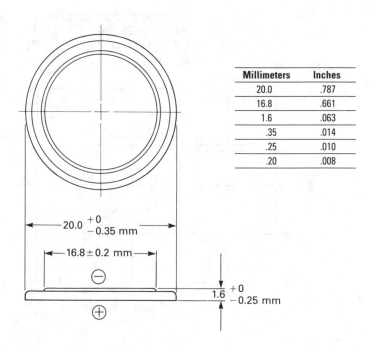

Millimeters	Inches
20.0	.787
16.8	.661
1.6	.063
.35	.014
.25	.010
.20	.008

20.0 $^{+0}_{-0.35}$ mm

16.8 ± 0.2 mm

1.6 $^{+0}_{-0.25}$ mm

Specifications

Voltage Taps	—, + 3
Terminals	Flat Contacts
Service Capacity	70mAh
Average Weight	1.9 grams (0.07 oz.)

Service data is on next page.

ENERCELL® Type CR2016H

Discharge Characteristics for Various Loads — 70°F (21.1°C)

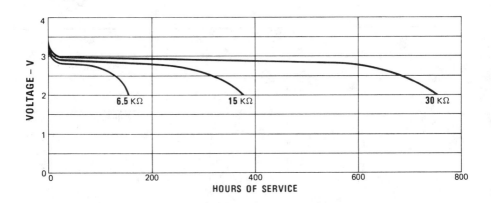

Discharge Characteristics for Various Temperatures

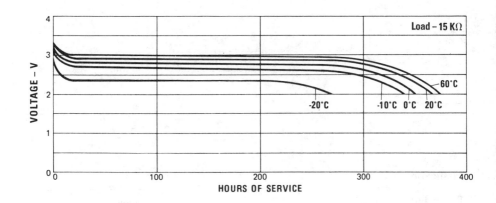

Type: **Lithium-Manganese Dioxide**
Suggested Current Range: **See Discharge Data**

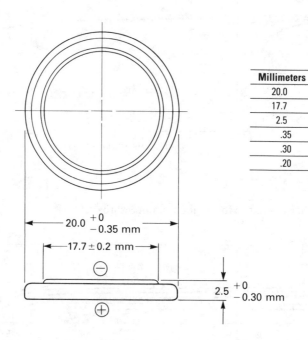

Millimeters	Inches
20.0	.787
17.7	.697
2.5	.098
.35	.014
.30	.012
.20	.008

20.0 $^{+0}_{-0.35}$ mm

17.7 ± 0.2 mm

⊖

⊕

2.5 $^{+0}_{-0.30}$ mm

Specifications

Voltage Taps	—, + 3
Terminals	Flat Contacts
Service Capacity	155mAh
Average Weight	2.5 grams (0.09 oz.)

Service data is on next page.

ENERCELL® Type CR2025

Discharge Characteristics for Various Loads — 70°F (21.1°C)

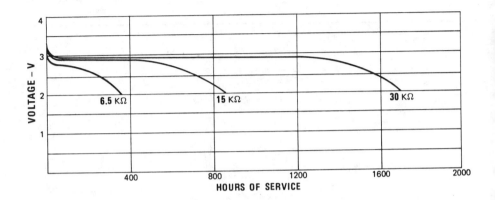

Discharge Characteristics for Various Temperatures

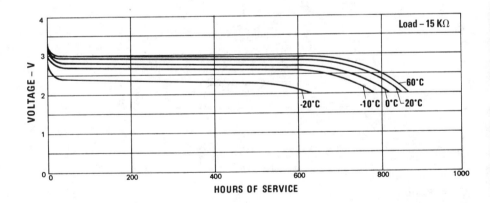

Type: **Lithium-Manganese Dioxide**
Suggested Current Range: **See Discharge Data**

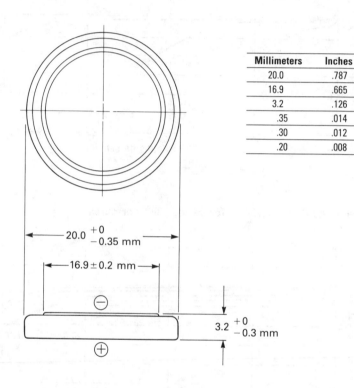

Millimeters	Inches
20.0	.787
16.9	.665
3.2	.126
.35	.014
.30	.012
.20	.008

$20.0 \begin{smallmatrix} +0 \\ -0.35 \end{smallmatrix}$ mm

16.9 ± 0.2 mm

$3.2 \begin{smallmatrix} +0 \\ -0.3 \end{smallmatrix}$ mm

Specifications

Voltage Taps	—, + 3
Terminals	Flat Contacts
Service Capacity	200mAh
Average Weight	3.0 grams (0.11 oz.)

Service data is on next page.

ENERCELL® Type CR2032

Discharge Characteristics for Various Loads — 70°F (21.1°C)

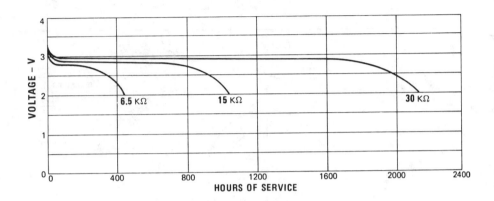

Discharge Characteristics for Various Temperatures

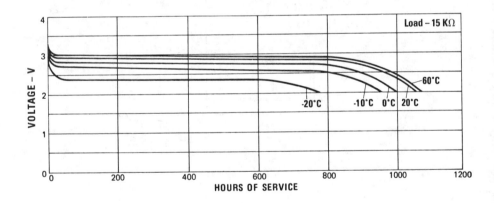

Type: **Lithium-Manganese Dioxide**
Suggested Current Range: **See Discharge Data**

Dimensions	
Millimeters	Inches
2.0	.48
12.3	.48
16.0	.630

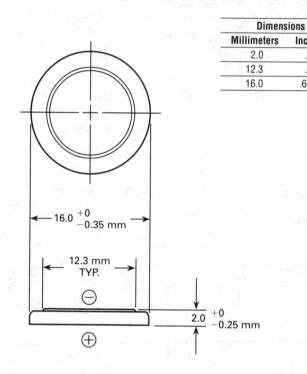

Specifications

Voltage Taps	−, + 3
Terminals	Flat Contacts
Service Capacity	50mAh
Average Weight	1.2 grams (0.04 oz.)

Service data is on the next page.

ENERCELL® Type CR1620

Discharge Characteristics for Various Loads – 70°F (21.1°C)

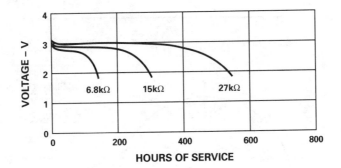

Discharge Characteristics for Various Temperatures

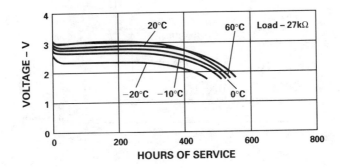

ENERCELL® Type CR2430

Catalog No. 23-166 — **3.0** VOLTS

Type: **Lithium-Manganese Dioxide**
Suggested Current Range: **See Discharge Data**

Dimensions	
Millimeters	**Inches**
3.0	.118
19.0	.748
24.5	.964

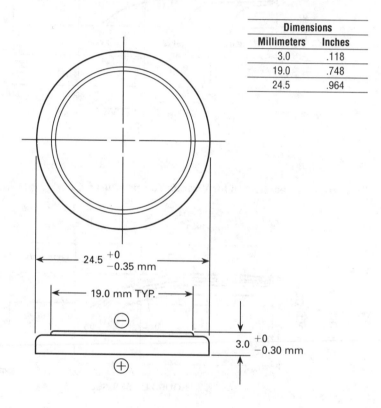

24.5 $^{+0}_{-0.35}$ mm

19.0 mm TYP.

3.0 $^{+0}_{-0.30}$ mm

Specifications

Voltage Taps	−, + 3
Terminals	Flat Contacts
Service Capacity	220mAh
Average Weight	3.9 grams (0.014 oz.)

Service data is on the next page.

ENERCELL® Type CR2430

Discharge Characteristics for Various Loads – 70°F (21.1°C)

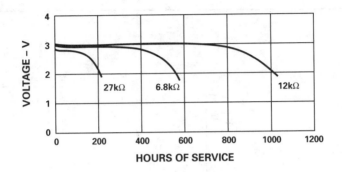

Discharge Characteristics for Various Temperatures

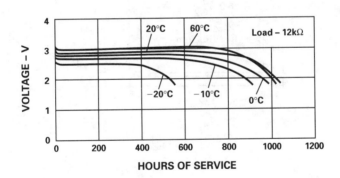

Type: **Lithium-Manganese Dioxide**
Suggested Current Range: **See Discharge Data**

Dimensions	
Millimeters	**Inches**
1.6	.063
13.8	.543
16.0	.630

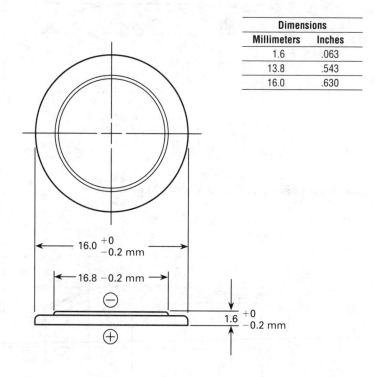

16.0 $^{+0}_{-0.2}$ mm

16.8 −0.2 mm

⊖

⊕

1.6 $^{+0}_{-0.2}$ mm

Specifications

Voltage Taps	−, + 3
Terminals	Flat Contacts
Service Capacity	42mAh
Average Weight	1.2 grams (0.04 oz.)

Service data is on the next page.

ENERCELL® Type CR1616

Discharge Characteristics for Various Loads – 70°F (21.1°C)

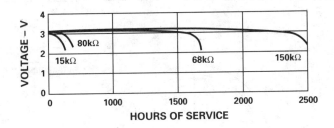

Discharge Characteristics for Various Temperatures

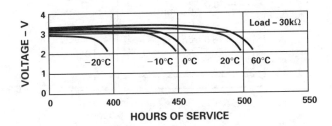

Type: **Lithium-Polycarbonmonofluoride**
Suggested Current Range: **See Discharge Data**

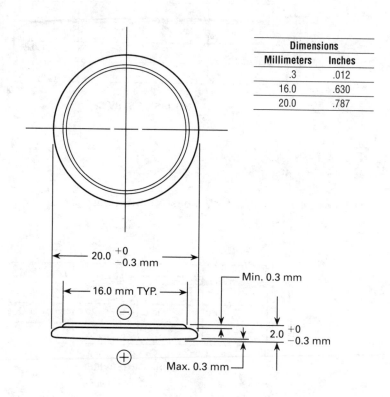

Dimensions	
Millimeters	**Inches**
.3	.012
16.0	.630
20.0	.787

20.0 $^{+0}_{-0.3}$ mm

16.0 mm TYP.

Min. 0.3 mm

2.0 $^{+0}_{-0.3}$ mm

Max. 0.3 mm

Specifications

Voltage Taps	−, + 3
Terminals	Flat Contacts
Service Capacity	80mAh
Average Weight	1.8 grams (0.04 oz.)

Service data is on the next page.

ENERCELL® Type BR2020

Estimated Average Hours Service at 70°F (21.1°C)

SCHEDULE	STARTING DRAIN (microamperes)	LOAD (ohms)	CUTOFF VOLTAGE 2.5V
Continuous	180	15kΩ	430

Discharge Characteristics – 70°F (21.1°C)

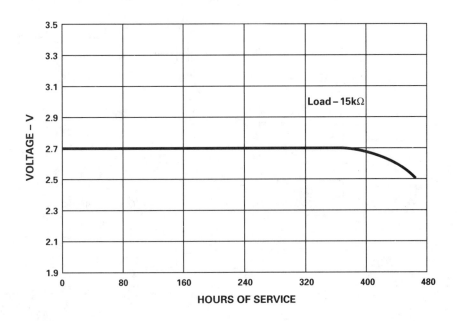

Load – 15kΩ

Internal Resistance

Fresh battery (1kHz, 10mA)   25 ohms maximum

Type: **Lithium-Polycarbonmonofluoride**
Suggested Current Range: **See Discharge Data**

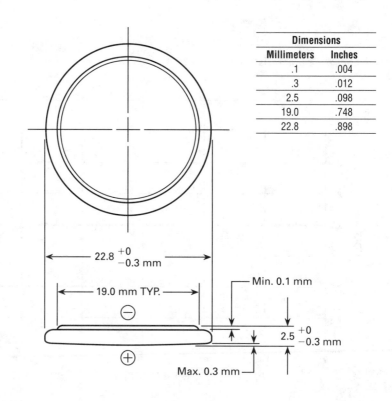

Dimensions	
Millimeters	**Inches**
.1	.004
.3	.012
2.5	.098
19.0	.748
22.8	.898

22.8 $^{+0}_{-0.3}$ mm

19.0 mm TYP.

⊖

⊕

Min. 0.1 mm

2.5 $^{+0}_{-0.3}$ mm

Max. 0.3 mm

Specifications

Voltage Taps	–, + 3
Terminals	Flat Contacts
Service Capacity	165mAh
Average Weight	3.0 grams (0.11 oz.)

Service data is on the next page.

ENERCELL® Type BR2325

Estimated Average Hours Service at 70°F (21.1°C)

SCHEDULE	STARTING DRAIN (microamperes)	LOAD (ohms)	CUTOFF VOLTAGE 2.5V
Continuous	180	15kΩ	920

Discharge Characteristics for Various Loads – 70°F (21.1°C)

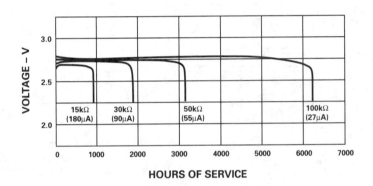

Discharge Characteristics for Various Temperatures

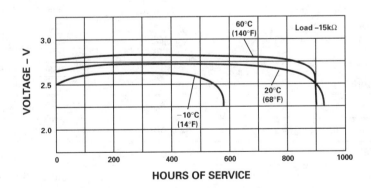

Internal Resistance

Fresh battery (1kHz, 10mA)   25 ohms maximum

ENERCELL® Type 675HPX

Type: **Zinc Air**
Applications: **Pagers/Hearing Aids**
Suggested Current Range: **See Discharge Data**

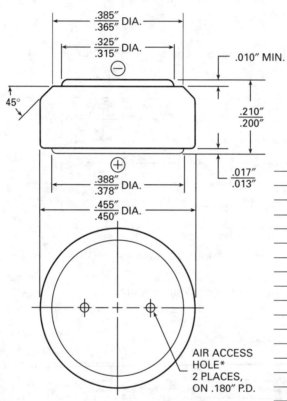

Dimensions	
Inches	**Millimeters**
.010	.25
.013	.33
.017	.43
.180	4.57
.200	5.08
.210	5.33
.315	8.00
.325	8.26
.365	9.27
.378	9.60
.385	9.78
.388	9.86
.450	11.43
.455	11.56

Specifications

Voltage Taps	−, + 1.45
Internal Impedance @ 1kHz	≤3.0 ohms
Average Weight	0.06 oz. (1.7 grams)
Displaced Volume	0.34 cubic inch (0.56 cubic centimeters)
Capacity	520mAh
Limiting Current @ 1.1V	12.0mA

Battery compartments must be designed to insure that atmospheric
oxygen may enter air holes and activate the cell.

Rev. 2/90

Service data is on the next page.

ENERCELL® Type 675HPX

Voltage Discharge Curve 675HPX
Load 620 Ohms 24 Hrs/Day
End Voltage: 0.9V

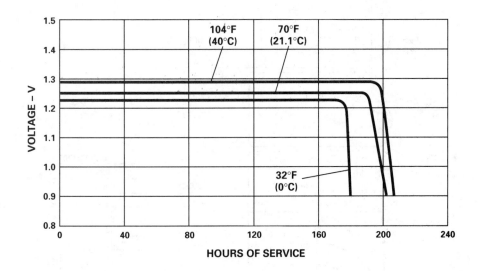

Type: **Zinc Air**
Applications: **Pagers/Hearing Aids**
Suggested Current Range: **See Discharge Data**

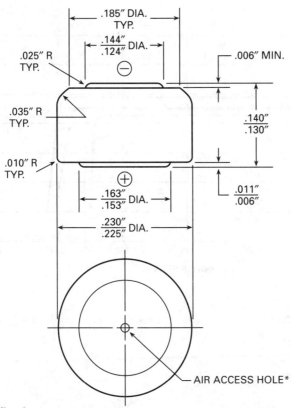

Dimensions	
Inches	**Millimeters**
.006	.15
.010	.25
.011	.28
.025	.64
.035	.89
.124	3.15
.130	3.30
.140	3.56
.144	3.66
.153	3.89
.163	4.14
.185	4.70
.225	5.72
.230	5.84

Specifications

Voltage Taps	−, + 1.45
Terminals	Flat Contacts
Average Weight	0.01 oz. (0.3 gram)
Capacity	50mAh
Internal Impedance @ 1kHz	≤16 ohms
Limiting Current @ 1.1V	2mA

Battery compartments must be designed to insure that atmospheric
oxygen may enter air holes and activate the cell.

Service data is on the next page.

ENERCELL® Type 230HPX

Voltage Discharge Curve 230HPX
Load 1,000 Ohms 24 Hrs/Day
End Voltage: 1.0V

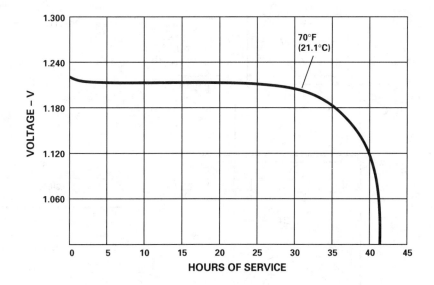

Type: **Zinc Air**
Applications: **Pagers/Hearing Aids**
Suggested Current Range: **See Discharge Data**

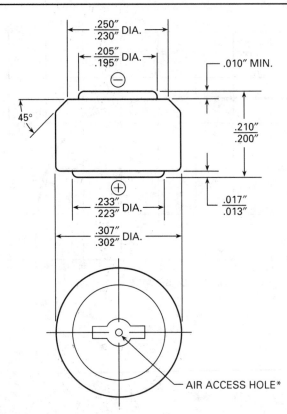

Dimensions	
Inches	**Millimeters**
.010	.25
.013	.33
.017	.43
.195	4.95
.200	5.08
.205	5.21
.210	5.33
.223	5.66
.230	5.84
.233	5.92
.250	6.35
.302	7.67
.307	7.80

AIR ACCESS HOLE*

Specifications

Voltage Taps	−, + 1.45
Internal Impedance @ 1kHz	≤5.0 ohms
Average Weight	0.03 oz. (0.8 gram)
Displaced Volume	0.16 cubic inch (0.26 cubic centimeter)
Capacity	200mAh
Limiting Current @ 1.1V	6.0mA

Battery compartments must be designed to insure that atmospheric
oxygen may enter air holes and activate the cell.

Rev. 2/90

Service data is on the next page.

ENERCELL® Type 13HPX

Voltage Discharge Curve 13HPX
Load 1,000 Ohms 24 Hrs/Day
End Voltage: 0.9V

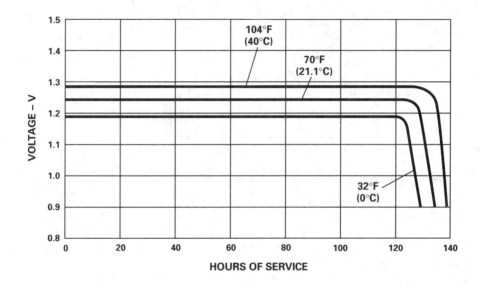

Type: **Zinc Air**
Applications: **Pagers/Hearing Aids**
Suggested Current Range: **See Discharge Data**

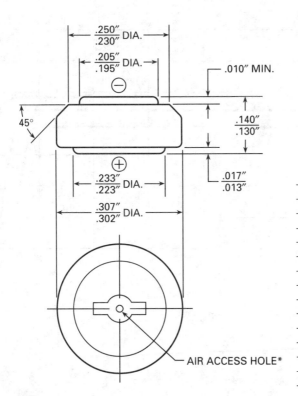

AIR ACCESS HOLE*

Dimensions	
Inches	Millimeters
.010	.25
.013	.33
.017	.43
.130	3.30
.140	3.56
.195	4.95
.205	5.21
.223	5.66
.230	5.84
.233	5.92
.250	6.35
.302	7.67
.307	7.80

Specifications

Voltage Taps	−, + 1.45
Internal Impedance @ 1kHz	≤5.0 ohms
Average Weight	0.02 oz. (0.5 gram)
Displaced Volume	0.010 cubic inch (0.17 cubic centimeter)
Capacity	90mAh
Limiting Current @ 1.1V	5.2mA

Battery compartments must be designed to insure that atmospheric
oxygen may enter air holes and activate the cell.

Rev. 2/90

Service data is on the next page.

ENERCELL® Type 312HPX

Voltage Discharge Curve 312HPX
Load 1,000 Ohms 24 Hrs/Day
End Voltage: 0.9V

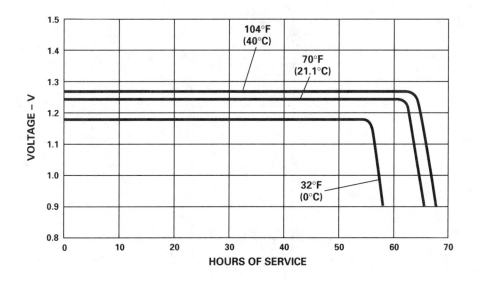

Type: **Alkaline-Manganese Dioxide**
Application: **Electronic Cigarette Lighters, Remote Controllers**
Suggested Current Range: **Pulsed Operation (Under 5mA for 1-2 seconds)**

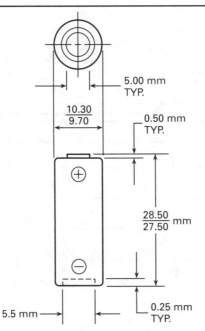

Dimensions	
Millimeters	Inches
.25	.010
.50	.020
5.50	.217
9.70	.382
10.00	.394
10.30	.406
27.50	1.083
28.50	1.122

Specifications

Voltage Taps	−, + 12
Terminals	Nickel plated — projecting positive (red); recessed negative (black)
Average Service Capacity (to 6.0V) (Rated Capacity at 20,000 ohms at 20°C within 30 days of manufacture)	28mAh
Average Weight	7.5 grams
Jacket	Metal
Shell Life	18 months

Interchangeability Guide

Replaces:
Colibri	2001
GP	23A
Ronson	VR22
Superpila	MS21
Win	EL12

Service data is on the next page.

Radio Shack Lighter Cell

Estimated Average Service at 70°F (21.1°C)

SCHEDULE	STARTING DRAIN (microamperes)	LOAD (ohms)	CUTOFF VOLTAGE 6.0V
8 hours/day 5 days/week	620	20,000	65 hours

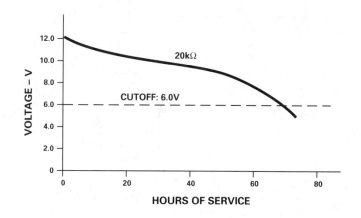

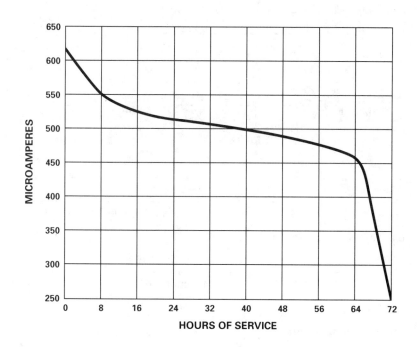

Type: **Nickel-Cadmium**
Application: **Cordless Telecommunications Equipment**
Suggested Current Range: **See Discharge Data**

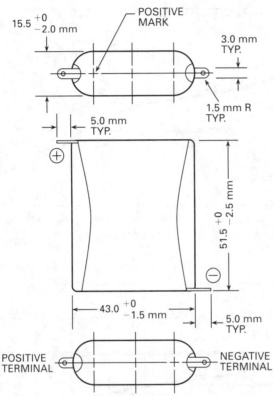

Dimensions	
Millimeters	**Inches**
1.5	.059
2.0	.079
2.5	.098
3.0	.118
5.0	.197
15.5	.610
43.0	1.69
51.5	2.03

Specifications

Voltage Taps	−, + 3.6
Terminals	Nickel Plated Solder Tabs
Average Service Capacity (to 3.0V)	600mAh
Average Weight	75 grams (2.75 oz.)
Volume	34.3 cubic centimeters (2.09 cubic inches)
Jacket	Insulated

Service data is on the next page.

ENERCELL® Telephone Battery Pack

Estimated Average Service at 77°F (25°C)

Charging Current	60mA
Charging Time	14-16 hours

Voltage Discharge Curve
Continuous load of 600mA to 3.0 volts.

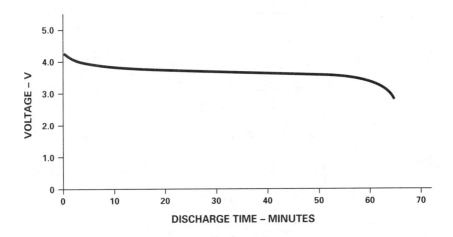

Type: **Nickel-Cadmium**
Application: **Cordless Telecommunications Equipment**
Suggested Current Range: **See Discharge Data**

Dimensions	
Millimeters	Inches
1.5	.059
2.0	.079
4.0	.157
10.0	.394
25.8	1.020
27.7	1.090

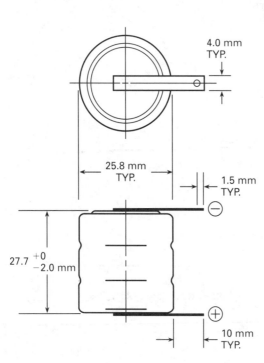

Specifications

Voltage Taps	−, + 3.6
Terminals	Nickel Plated Solder Tabs
Average Service Capacity (to 3.0V)	280mAh
Average Weight	39 grams (1.43 oz.)
Jacket	Insulated

Service data is on the next page.

ENERCELL® Telephone Battery Pack

Estimated Average Service at 10°C–45°C (50°F–113°F)

Charging Current and Time	Current	Time
Nominal	28mA	14 hours
Trickle Charge	2.8mA	Continuous
Intermittent Trickle	8.4mA	Intermittent

Norminal Charging Voltage	4.0–4.5 volts

Discharging Current and Time Mean Voltage = 3.5V End Voltage = 3.0V	Current	Time
Nominal	56mA	5 hours

Battery Life per IEC 509	
IEC cycles for test	800–1000
Charge Period	35mA for 6 hours 20 minutes
Discharge Period	35mA for 4 hours 40 minutes
Capacity at end (minimum)	168mAh

Type: **Nickel-Cadmium**
Application: **Cordless Telecommunications Equipment**
Suggested Current Range: **See Discharge Data**

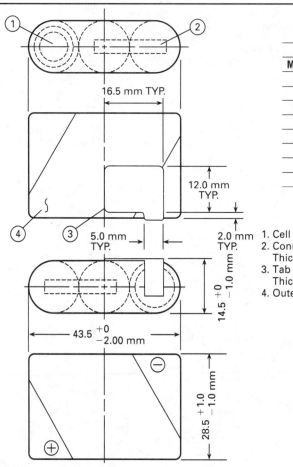

Dimensions	
Millimeters	**Inches**
1.0	.039
2.0	.079
5.0	.197
12.0	.472
14.5	.571
16.5	.650
28.5	1.120
43.5	1.710

1. Cell
2. Connecting Tab
   Thickness – 0.2mm (typ.)
3. Tab Contact
   Thickness – 0.15 mm (typ.)
4. Outer Jacket

Specifications

Voltage Taps	–, + 3.6
Terminals	Nickel Plated Side Tab and Flat Contact
Average Service Capacity (to 3.0V)	250mAh
Average Weight	40 grams (1.47 oz.)
Jacket	Insulated

Service data is on the next page.

ENERCELL® Telephone Battery Pack

Estimated Average Service at 68±9°F (20±5°C)

Charging Current and Time	Current	Time
Nominal	25mA	15 hours
Trickle Charge	8.3mA	Continuous
Quick Charge	62.5mA	6 hours
Discharging Current		
Maximum	500mA	
Nominal	50mA	5 hours
(End Voltage = 3.0V)		
Battery Life		
Cycles		500
Charge Period		30 mA for 6 hours
Discharge Period		62.5 mA for 2 hours
Capacity at end (minimum)		125mAh
(50mA discharge to 3.0V)		
Trickle		
Charge Period		8.3mA for 2 years Continuous
Capacity at end (minimum)		
(50mA discharge to 3.0V)		125mAh

ENERCELL® Telephone Battery Pack

Type: **Nickel-Cadmium**
Application: **Cordless Telecommunications Equipment**
Suggested Current Range: **See Discharge Data**

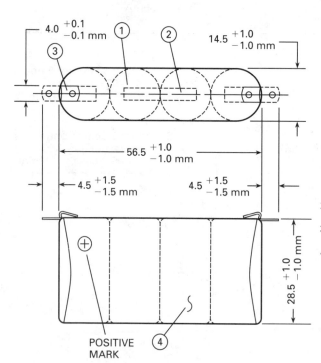

Dimensions	
Millimeters	**Inches**
.1	.004
1.0	.039
1.5	.059
4.0	.157
4.5	.177
14.5	.571
28.5	1.120
56.5	2.220

1. Cell
2. Connecting Tab
   Thickness – 0.15 mm (typ.)
3. Soldering Tab
   Thickness – 0.15 mm (typ.)
4. Outer Jacket

Specifications

Voltage Taps	–, + 4.8
Terminals	Nickel Plated Solder Tabs
Average Service Capacity (to 4.0V)	270mAh
Average Weight	52 grams (1.91 oz.)
Jacket	Insulated

Service data is on the next page.

ENERCELL® Telephone Battery Pack

Estimated Average Service at 68±9°F (20±5°C)

Charging Current and Time	Current	Time
Nominal	27mA	15 hours
Trickle Charge	9.0mA	Continuous
Quick Charge	67.5mA	6 hours
Discharging Current		
Maximum	540mA	
Nominal	54mA	5 hours
(End Voltage = 3.0V)		
Battery Life		
Cycles		500
Charge Period		32.4mA for 6 hours
Discharge Period		67.5mA for 2 hours
Capacity at end (minimum)		135mAh
(54mA discharge to 4.0V)		
Trickle		
Charge Period		9.0mA for 2 years Continuous
Capacity at end (minimum)		
(54mA discharge to 4.0V)		135mAh

Type: **Nickel-Cadmium**
Application: **Cordless Telecommunications Equipment**
Suggested Current Range: **See Discharge Data**

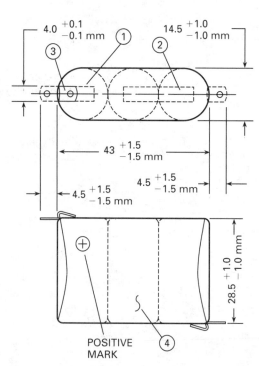

Dimensions	
Millimeters	Inches
.1	.004
1.0	.039
4.0	.157
4.5	.177
14.5	.571
28.5	1.120
43.0	1.690

1. Cell
2. Connecting Tab
   Thickness – 0.15 mm (typ.)
3. Soldering Tab
   Thickness – 0.15 mm (typ.)
4. Outer Jacket

POSITIVE
MARK

Specifications

Voltage Taps	–, + 3.6
Terminals	Nickel Plated Solder Tabs
Average Service Capacity (to 3.0V)	270mAh
Average Weight	39 grams (1.43 oz.)
Jacket	Insulated

Service data is on the next page.

ENERCELL® Telephone Battery Pack

Estimated Average Service at 68±9°F (20±5°C)

Charging Current and Time	Current	Time
Nominal	27mA	15 hours
Trickle Charge	9mA	Continuous
Quick Charge	67.5mA	6 hours

Discharging Current		
Maximum	500mA	
Nominal		
(End voltage = 3.0V)	54mA	5 hours

Battery Life	
Cycles	500
Charge Period	32.4 mA for 6 hours
Discharge Period	67.5 mA for 2 hours
Capacity at end (minimum)	135mAh
(54mA discharge to 3.0V)	
Trickle	
Charge Period	9.0 mA for 2 years Continuous
Capacity at end (minimum)	135mAh
(54mA discharge to 3.0V)	

Discharge Characteristics for Various Loads

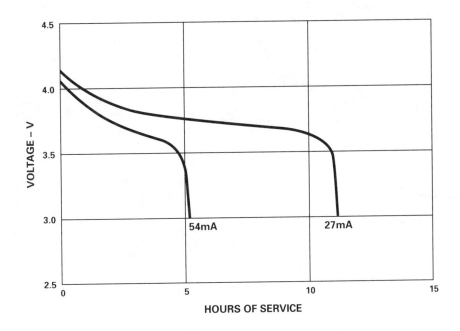

ENERCELL® Telephone Battery Pack

Type: **Nickel-Cadmium**
Application: **Cordless Telecommunications Equipment**
Suggested Current Range: **See Discharge Data**

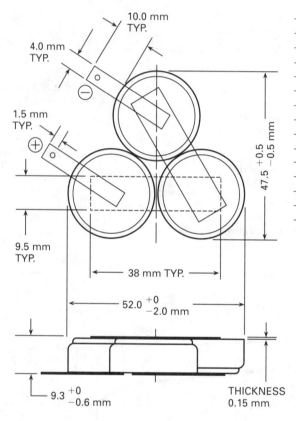

Dimensions	
Millimeters	Inches
.15	.006
.5	.020
.6	.024
1.5	.059
2.0	.079
4.0	.157
9.3	.366
9.5	.374
10.0	.394
38.0	1.500
47.5	1.870
52.0	2.050

Specifications

Voltage Taps	−, + 3.6
Terminals	Nickel Plated Solder Tabs
Average Service Capacity (to 3.0V)	280mAh
Average Weight	39 grams (1.43 oz.)
Jacket	Insulated

Service data is on the next page.

ENERCELL® Telephone Battery Pack

Estimated Average Service at 10°C–45°C (50°F–113°F)

Charging Current and Time	Current	Time
Nominal	28mA	14 hours
Trickle Charge	2.8mA	Continuous
Intermittent Charge	8.4mA	Intermittent

Nominal Charging Voltage	4.0–4.5 volts

Discharging Current and Time (Mean Voltage = 3.5V, End Voltage = 3.0V)	Current	Time
Nominal	56mA	5 hours

Battery Life per IEC 509	
IEC Cycles for Test	800–1000
Charge Period	35 mA for 6 hours 20 minutes
Discharge Period	35 mA for 4 hours 40 minutes
Capacity at end (minimum)	168mAh

Type: **Alkaline-Manganese Dioxide**
Application: **Specialty Items**
Suggested Current Range: **See Discharge Data**

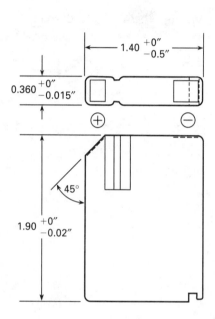

Dimensions	
Inches	**Millimeters**
.015	.38
.020	.50
.345	8.76
.360	9.14
1.380	35.05
1.400	35.56
1.880	47.75
1.900	48.26

Specifications

Voltage Taps	−, + 6
Terminals	Top and Diagonal Side Recessed Flat Contacts
Average Service Capacity (to 3.2V)	550mAh
Average Weight	1.2 oz. (34.0 grams)
Volume	0.92 cubic inch (15.0 cubic centimeters)
Jacket	Insulated

Service data is on the next page.

ENERCELL® Type 7K67 Photo Battery Pack

Estimated Average Service at 70°F (21.1°C)

SCHEDULE	STARTING DRAIN (milliamperes)	LOAD (ohms)	CUTOFF VOLTAGE 3.2V
Continuous	14	340	40 hours

Continuous Average Discharge Characteristics for Various Loads — 70°F (21.1°C)

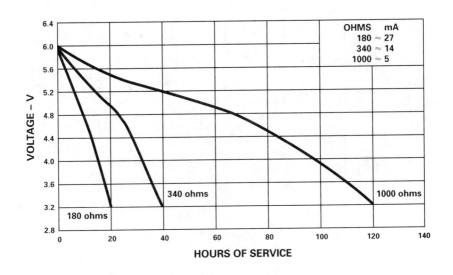

Type: **Lithium-Polycarbonmonofluoride**
Application: **Cameras, Personal Computer Memory Backup**
Suggested Current Range: **See Discharge Data**

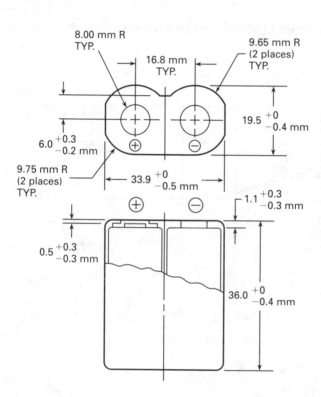

Dimensions	
Millimeters	**Inches**
.20	.008
.30	.012
.40	.010
.50	.020
1.10	.043
6.00	.236
8.00	.315
9.65	.380
9.75	.384
16.8	.661
19.5	.768
33.9	1.335
36.0	1.417

Specifications

Voltage Taps	−, + 6
Terminals	Flat Contacts
Average Service Capacity (to 3.6V)	1200mAh
Average Weight	31 grams (1.14 oz.)
Jacket	Insulated

Service data is on the next page.

ENERCELL® Type BRP2

Continuous Average Discharge Characteristics for Various Loads —
20 ± 2°C (68 ± 3.6°F)

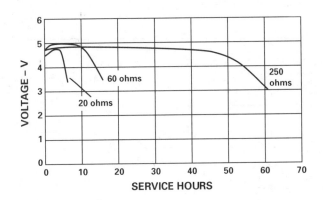

Continuous Average Discharge Characteristics for Various Temperatures

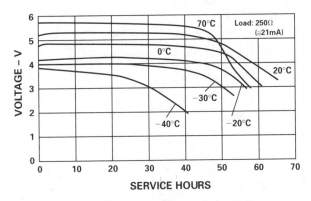

Pulsed Average Discharge Characteristics for Various Temperatures
Conditions: Load of 0.5A ON for 4 Seconds, OFF for 36 Seconds

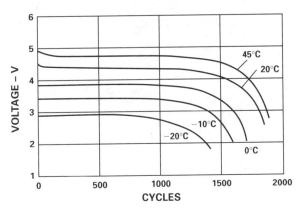

Type: Lithium-Manganese Dioxide
Application: Cameras, Personal Computers, Security and Emergency Equipment
Suggested Current Range: See Discharge Data

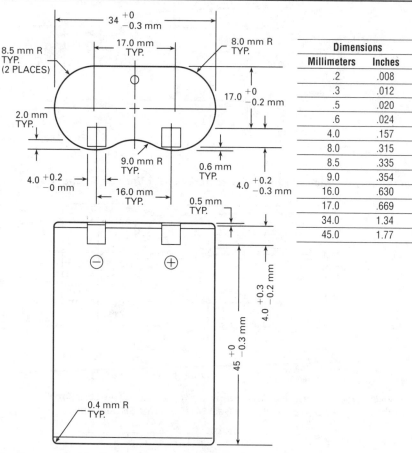

Dimensions	
Millimeters	Inches
.2	.008
.3	.012
.5	.020
.6	.024
4.0	.157
8.0	.315
8.5	.335
9.0	.354
16.0	.630
17.0	.669
34.0	1.34
45.0	1.77

Specifications

Voltage Taps	−, + 6
Terminals	Side Tabs – Nickel Plated
Average Service Capacity (to 4.0V)	1300mAh
Average Weight	40 grams (1.47 oz.)
Jacket	Insulated

Service data is on the next page.

ENERCELL® Type 2CR5 Photo Battery Pack

Estimated Average Service at 23 ± 2°C (73.4 ± 3.6°F)

SCHEDULE	STARTING DRAIN (milliamperes)	LOAD (ohms)	CUTOFF VOLTAGE 4.0V
24 hour/day	14	400	95 hours

Continuous Average Discharge Characteristics for Various Temperatures

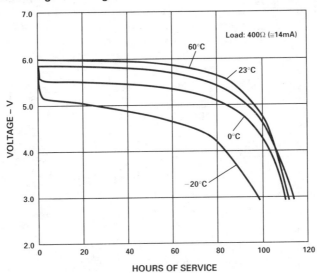

Pulsed Average Discharge Characteristics for Various Temperatures
Conditions: Load of 1.2A ON for 3 Seconds, OFF for 7 Seconds

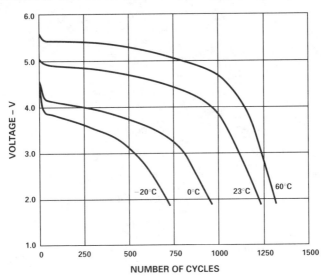

Type: **Lithium-Manganese Dioxide**
Application: **Cameras, Personal Computers, Security and Emergency Equipment**
Suggested Current Range: **See Discharge Data**

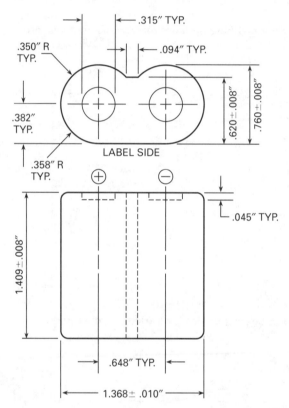

LABEL SIDE

Dimensions	
Inches	Millimeters
.008	.203
.010	.254
.045	1.14
.094	2.39
.315	8.00
.350	8.89
.358	9.09
.382	9.70
.620	15.75
.648	16.46
.760	19.30
1.368	34.75
1.409	35.79

Specifications

Voltage Taps	−, + 6
Terminals	Nickel Plated – Flat Contacts
Average Service Capacity (to 4.0V)	1250mAh
Average Weight	1.58 oz. (45 grams)
Volume	1.5 cubic inches (24 cubic centimeters)
Jacket	Insulated

Service data is on the next page.

ENERCELL® Type DL223A/CRP2 Photo Battery Pack

Estimated Average Service at 70°F (21.1°C)

SCHEDULE	STARTING DRAIN (milliamperes)	LOAD (ohms)	CUTOFF VOLTAGE 4.0V
24 hours/day	25	200	50 hours

Continuous Average Discharge Characteristics for Various Temperatures

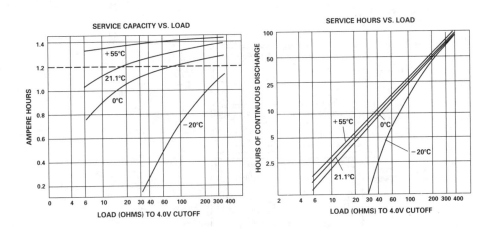

Pulsed Average Discharge Characteristics for Various Temperatures
Conditions: Load of 0.9A ON for 3 Seconds, OFF for 27 Seconds

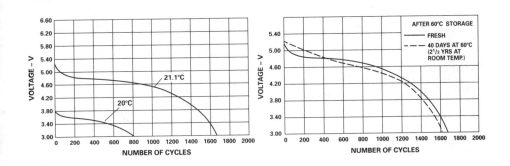

Type: **Sealed Lead Acid**
Suggested Current Range: **See Discharge Data**

Dimensions	
Inches	Millimeters
1.78	45
2.75	70
4.43	113

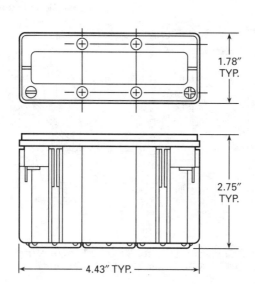

1.78"
TYP.

2.75"
TYP.

4.43" TYP.

Specifications

Voltage Taps	−, + 6
Terminals	Male Spade .187" × .025"
Average Service Capacity (at 250mA discharge rate)	2500mAh
Average Weight	1.2 lbs. (540 grams)
Case	Rigid Plastic

Service data is on the next page.

ENERCELL® Sealed Rechargeable Lead Acid

Rated Capacity
    One hour rate (C rate)   1.8Ah (2.5A)
    Ten hour rate (C/10 rate)   2.5Ah (250mA)
    Twenty hour rate (C/20 rate)   2.7Ah (125mA)

Charging

	Constant Voltage	Constant Current
Cyclic	7.2–7.8V	Max C/3 rate
Float	6.9–7.2V	Max C/500 rate

Cell Temperature Limits (°C)
    Storage   −65°C to +65°C
    Discharge   −65°C to +65°C
    Charge   −40°C to +65°C

Storage Time at Ambient
    0°C   7200 days
    23°C   1200 days
    65°C   60 days

Cycle Life
    200 cycles –   100% depth of discharge, one cycle per day: 7.35V constant
                      voltage charge – no current limit; Discharge: C/5 rate.
    2000 cycles – 25% depth of discharge (charge 7.35V for 7.5 hours – 2.0A current
                      limit; Discharge: C/2 rate for 30 minutes.)

Internal Resistance
    Max @ Charged Cell 10×10^{-3} ohms

ENERCELL® Sealed Rechargeable Lead Acid

Discharge Characteristics at 25°C

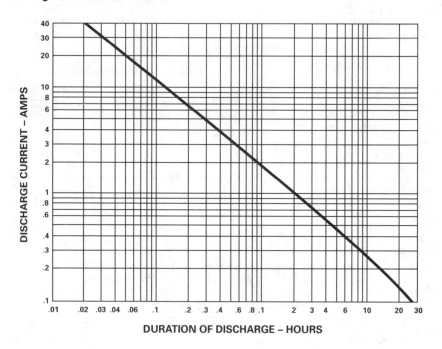

DURATION OF DISCHARGE – HOURS

State of Charge

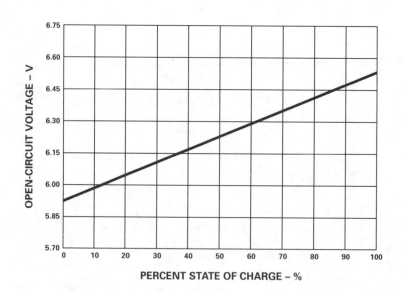

PERCENT STATE OF CHARGE – %

ENERCELL® Sealed Rechargeable Lead Acid

Storage Characteristics

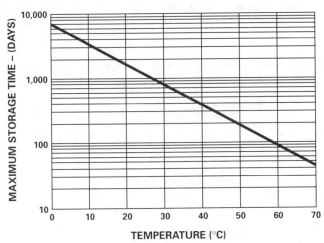

Voltage Regulation

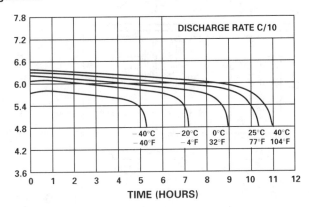

Temperature Characteristics

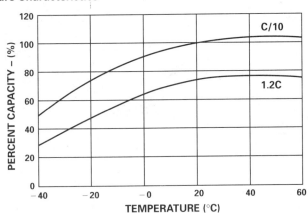

Type: **Sealed Lead Acid**
Suggested Current Range: **See Discharge Data**

Dimensions	
Inches	Millimeters
2.11	54
3.02	77
5.47	139

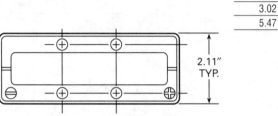

2.11"
TYP.

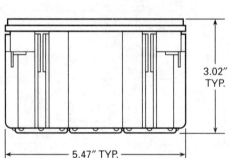

3.02"
TYP.

◄─── 5.47" TYP. ───►

Specifications

Voltage Taps	−, + 6
Terminals	Male Spade .187" × .025"
Average Service Capacity (at 500mA discharge rate)	5000mAh
Average Weight	2.43 lbs. (1110 grams)
Case	Rigid Plastic

Service data is on the next page.

ENERCELL® Sealed Rechargeable Lead Acid

Rated Capacity	
One hour rate (C rate)	3.2Ah (5.0A)
Ten hour rate (C/10 rate)	5.0Ah (500mA)
Twenty hour rate (C/20 rate)	5.4Ah (250mA)

Charging

	Constant Voltage	Constant Current
Cyclic	7.2–7.8V	Max C/3 rate
Float	6.9–7.2V	Max C/500 rate

Cell Temperature Limits (°C)	
Storage	−65°C to +65°C
Discharge	−65°C to +65°C
Charge	−40°C to +65°C

Storage Time at Ambient	
0°C	7200 days
23°C	1200 days
65°C	60 days

Cycle Life

200 cycles – 100% depth of discharge, one cycle per day: 7.35V constant voltage charge – no current limit; Discharge: C/5 rate.

2000 cycles – 25% depth of discharge (charge 7.35V for 7.5 hours – 2.0A current limit; Discharge: C/2 rate for 30 minutes.)

Internal Resistance	
Max @ Charged Cell	5×10^{-3} ohms

ENERCELL® Sealed Rechargeable Lead Acid

Discharge Characteristics at 25°C

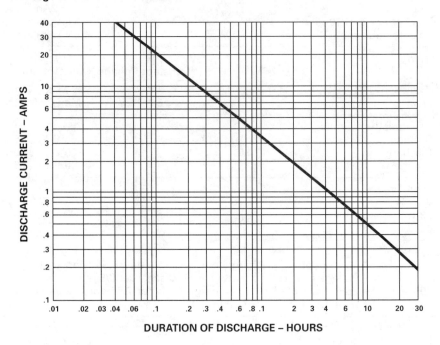

State of Charge

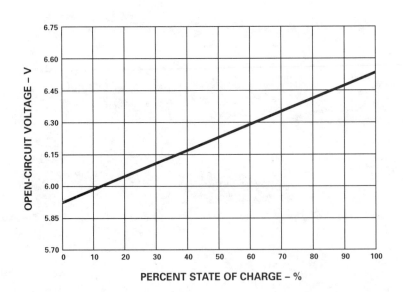

ENERCELL® Sealed Rechargeable Lead Acid

Storage Characteristics

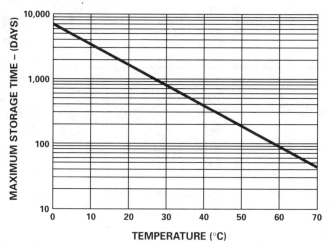

Voltage Regulation

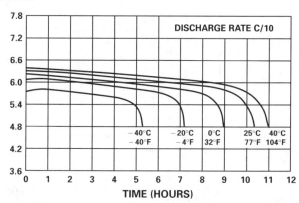

Temperature Characteristics

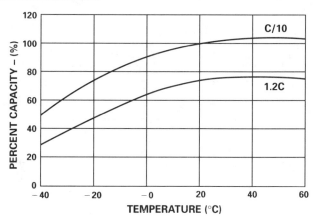

Catalog No. 23-230   **2.2** VOLTS

Type: **Nickel-Cadmium**
Application: **Radio Controlled Racing Cars**
Suggested Current Range: **See Discharge Data**

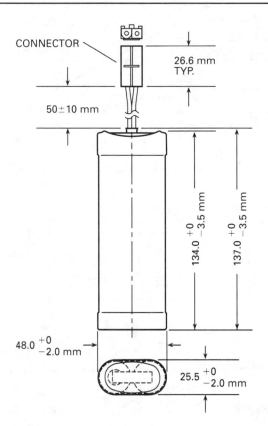

Dimensions	
Millimeters	Inches
2.0	.079
3.5	.138
10.0	.394
25.5	1.00
26.6	1.05
48	1.89
50	1.97
134	5.28
137	5.39

Specifications

Voltage Taps	−, + 7.2
Terminals	Connector – JST LR-02F-1
Average Service Capacity (to 6.0V)	1200mAh
Average Weight	320 grams (11.73 oz.)
Jacket	Insulated

Service data is on the next page.

ENERCELL® Turbo Racing Battery Pack

Estimated Average Service at 70°F (21.1°C)

SCHEDULE	STARTING DRAIN (milliamperes)	LOAD (ohms)	CUTOFF VOLTAGE 6.0V
Continuous	240		5 hours
Continuous	1200		50 minutes

Discharging Characteristics

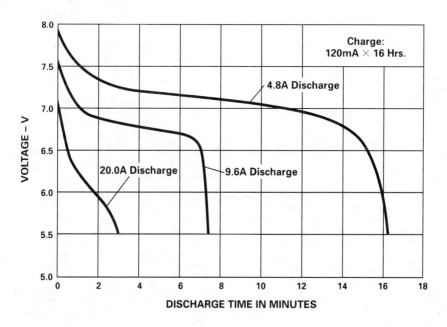

Battery Life   500 cycles
  Cycles for Test
    Charge Period   120 mA for 11 hours
    Discharge Period   840 mA for 1 hour
    Capacity at end (minimum)   720mAh

BATTERY TERMINOLOGY

Some of the terminology used in the battery industry is different than what we encounter everyday. In some cases it is even different than what we use in circuit design and application. Here is a glossary of common battery terminology for your reference.

Ah: see Ampere Hours.

Ampere-Hours (Ah): The product of current (amperes), multiplied by the time (hours) that current is flowing from the battery into a circuit. The capacity of a battery is expressed in ampere-hours.

Anode: The electrode at which an oxidation reaction occurs which is the negative electrode of an electrochemical galvanic cell. The electrode which exhibits loss of e lectrons.

Average Drain: The average current drawn from a battery during discharge. Approximated by calculating the current when the battery is discharged 50%.

Battery: May consist of one, two or more series or parallel cells connected internally.

C-Rate: Used for Nickel-Cadmium batteries. The discharge or charge current rate in amperes numerically equivalent to the rated capacity of the battery in ampere-hours. (Also see charge rate.)

Capacity: The current in amperes available from a fully charged battery for discharge over a period of time (hours) expressed in ampere-hours (Ah).

Cathode: The electrode at which a reduction reaction occurs (gain of 36-40 electrons). The positive electrode in an electrochemical galvanic cell. In secondary cells, either electrode may become the cathode, depending upon the direction of current flow.

CCV: See Closed Circuit Voltage.

Cell: An electrochemical system consisting of positive and negative electrodes, separator and electrolyte that is capable of converting chemical energy directly into electrical energy.

Cell Reversal: A condition whereby the polarity of the battery terminals is reversed due to overdischarge.

Charge Rate: The current at which a secondary battery is charged. It is usually expressed as a function of the battery's capacity. For example the 10-hour charge rate of 5 ampere-hour battery is $C/10 = 5Ah/10h = 0.5A = 500$ mA.

Charge Retention: The ability of a charged battery to resist self-discharge.

Charge, State of: The remaining charge of a battery at a given point in time in terms of its rated capacity.

Charging: Delivering electric energy to a battery for conversion to store chemical energy.

Closed Circuit Voltage (CCV): Voltage of a battery at a specific load.

Constant Current Charging: Method for charging secondary batteries in which current does not charge regardless of the battery voltage or temperature.

Constant Potential (CP): Method for charging secondary batteries with a fixed voltage.

CP: See Constant Potential.

Cutoff Voltage: Battery terminal voltage at which a discharge or charge is terminated.

Cycle: One sequence of charge and discharge of a secondary cell.

Cycle Life: In a secondary cell, the number of charge-discharge cycles the battery will experience before its capacity is lowered to the point where it is no longer useful.

Cylindrical Cell: A cell whose height is larger than its diameter.

Deep Discharge: Discharging of a battery to a specific cutoff voltage at a low current rate. Discharge cut-off voltage for Nickel-Cadmium batteries is considered to be 0.5 volts.

Depth of Discharge (DOD): The amount of discharged capacity expressed as a percentage or the rated capacity.

Discharge Rate: The current at which a battery is discharged.

Discharging: The withdrawal of electrical energy from a battery.

DOD: See Depth of Discharge.

Drain: Withdrawal of current from a battery.

Dry Battery: A type of battery where the electrolyte is immobilized either as a paste or gel or absorbed in the separator.

DTC: See Dumped Timed Charge.

Dumped-Time Charge (DTC): A charging method for secondary batteries where the discharge is at a rate-time combination equal to or greater than the corresponding charge rate-time combination.

Duty Cycle: The conditions to which a battery is subjected to during its use or test. Normal specified conditions are temperature, time, load, or current.

Eo: See Equivalent No-load Voltage.

Effective Internal Resistance (Re): The resistive opposition to current flow inside the battery causing a drop on battery terminal voltage proportional to current drain. Re varies with battery design, state of charge, temperature and age.

Electrode: The conducting body and active material at which the electrochemical reaction occurs.

Electrolyte: Fluid, gel or paste that serves as the media for movement of ions between the electrodes, usually an aqueous salt solution.

End-of-Charge-Voltage: The voltage of a Nickel-Cadmium battery at the end of the charge cycle just prior to terminating the charge.

End-of-Discharge-Voltage: The voltage of a battery at the end of the discharge cycle just prior to terminating the discharge.

ENERCELL®: The registered trademark for Radio Shack batteries.

Energy: Ampere hour capacity times average closed circuit discharge voltage expressed as watt-hours.

Energy Density: The stored energy to weight or volume ratio (watt-hours/pounds or watt-hours/ in^3) that is discharge rate dependent.

Entrainment: Conditions where gases generated in a vented cell carry the electrolyte out through the vent cap.

Environmental Conditions: External conditions in which a battery is used, such as ambient temperature, humidity, altitude, shock or vibration.

Equivalent Circuit: A circuit used to simulate the electrical characteristics of a battery.

Equivalent No-Load Voltage (Eo): Value of the open circuit source voltage in the equivalent circuit.

Fading: The loss of capability as the battery is used.

Failure: A condition at which a battery no longer may perform its intended function.

Fast Charging: Rapid charging of a Nickel-Cadmium battery at its C-rate or greater.

FEP: See Functional End Point.

Float Charging: Charging of a secondary battery with a continuous constant voltage supply that maintains the battery in a full-charge condition.

Functional End Point (FE): Voltage below which the battery operated component will not operate properly.

Imp: See Maximum-Power Discharge Current.

Impedance (Z): The opposition to ac current offered by a circuit (battery). Z is a combination of resistance and reactance.

Initial Drain: The starting current drain that a battery supplies when first put on load.

Internal Resistance (Ri): See Effective Internal Resistance (Re).

KOH: The chemical symbol for potassium hydroxide.

Maximum-Power Discharge Current (Imp): The current discharge rate at which the battery terminal voltage is equal to 1/2 of Eo and at which maximum power is transferred to the battery load.

Memory Effect: A phenomenon in which a Nickel-Cadmium battery, when successively cycled at identical depth of discharges, renders the balance of its capacity inaccessible at normal voltage levels.

Midpoint Voltage: The battery voltage at the halfway point between the fully charged state and the fully discharged condition.

Miniature Cell: A button cell whose diameter is greater than its height.

Negative Electrode: The electrode in a cell that has a negative voltage potential in reference to the other electrode during normal operating conditions.

Ni-Cd: Ni is the chemical symbol for nickel, Cd is cadmium. Ni-Cd is used as an abbreviation for nickel-cadmium.

Nominal Voltage: The midpoint battery voltage during discharge at a selected rate.

OCV: See Open-Circuit Voltage.

Open Circuit Voltage (OCV): Battery voltage at no load.

Overcharging: Continuing charge of a secondary battery after maximum charge. In a sealed battery, the result is increased battery temperature and internal pressure.

Oxidation: During discharge, the release of electrons by the battery's active material to the external circuit.

Oxygen Recombination: The process in Nickel-Cadmium batteries in which oxygen generated at the positive plate at the negative plate at the same rate, resulting in internally generated heat.

Plates: Common term for electrodes.

Positive Electrode: Has a positive voltage potential in reference to the other electrode in a cell during normal operating conditions.

Primary Battery: A battery designed to deliver the rated capacity once, then be discarded. It is not capable of being fully recharged.

Quick Charge: Charging rates for Nickel-Cadmium batteries ranging from 0.2C to 0.5C rate.

Re: See Effective Internal Resistance.

Ri: See Internal Resistance.

Recharge: The return of electrical energy to a battery.

Rechargeable Battery: A battery capable of being recharged, also called secondary batteries.

Reduction: The gain of electrons to the active material in a battery.

Sealed Dry Battery: A battery that is maintenance-free and can be operated in any position.

Secondary Battery: A battery which is capable of repeated discharge/charge cycles by using internal electrochemical reactions that are reversible.

Self-Discharge Rate: The rate at which a battery loses rated ampere hour capacity when not being used.

Service Maintenance: The percentage of rated capacity remaining after a specified period of time.

Shelf Life: The length of time a battery not in use will retain a specified amount of its rated capacity.

Slow Charge: Overnight charging of Nickel-Cadmium battery at 0.05C to 0.1C rate.

Standby Charge: A low overcharge current rate continuously applied to a battery to keep it at full charge, often called "tickle charge."

Starting Drain: See Initial Drain.

State of Charge: Remaining capacity expressed in terms of fully charged capacity.

Thermal Runaway: A condition in which a battery on continuous charge at elevated temperatures will destroy itself due to internal heating caused by high ambient temperature and/or high overcharge currents.

Trickle Charge: See Standby Charge.

Z: See Impedance.

INDEX